THE TEEN YEARS
EXPLAINED

A GUIDE TO HEALTHY ADOLESCENT DEVELOPMENT

By
Clea McNeely, MA, DrPH
Jayne Blanchard

With a foreword by
Nicole Yohalem
Karen Pittman

CONTENTS

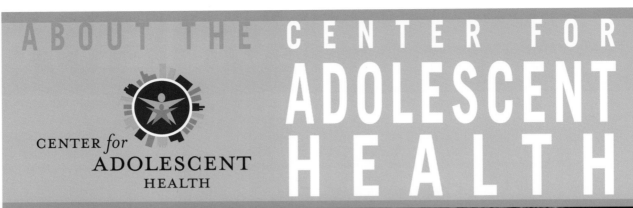

ABOUT THE CENTER FOR ADOLESCENT HEALTH

CENTER *for*
ADOLESCENT
HEALTH

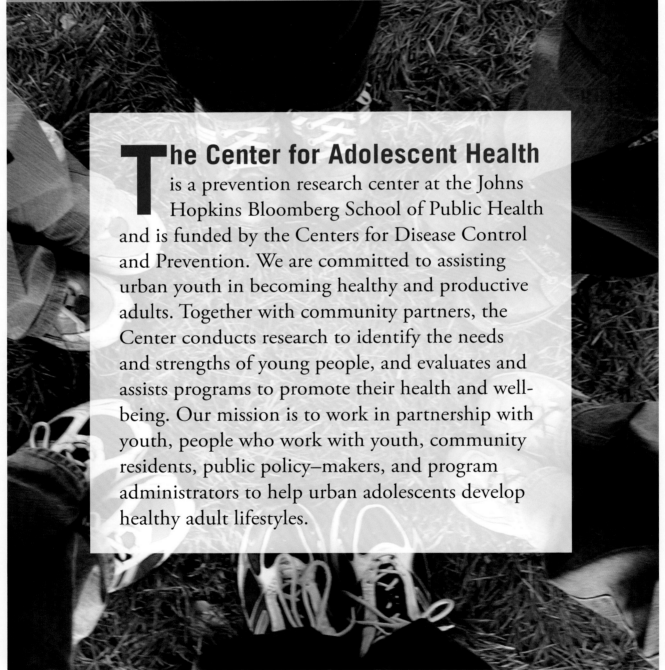

The Center for Adolescent Health is a prevention research center at the Johns Hopkins Bloomberg School of Public Health and is funded by the Centers for Disease Control and Prevention. We are committed to assisting urban youth in becoming healthy and productive adults. Together with community partners, the Center conducts research to identify the needs and strengths of young people, and evaluates and assists programs to promote their health and well-being. Our mission is to work in partnership with youth, people who work with youth, community residents, public policy–makers, and program administrators to help urban adolescents develop healthy adult lifestyles.

ACKNOWLEDGMENTS

The authors of *The Teen Years Explained: A Guide to Healthy Adolescent Development* would like to express our sincere gratitude to the following people for all of their guidance and support during the creation of this book:

Freya Sonenstein, PhD   **Nicole Yohalem**   **Karen Pittman**

The Guide was made possible by funding from the Centers for Disease Control and Prevention (CDC) to the Center for Adolescent Health at the Johns Hopkins Bloomberg School of Public Health, a member of the Prevention Research Centers Program (CDC cooperative agreement 1-U48-DP-000040). We would also like to thank the Charles Crane Family Foundation and the Shapiro Family Foundation for their support for the Guide.

Members of the Scientific Advisory Board

The Scientific Advisory Board provided insight and information in their professional review of the chapters. We thank them for their invaluable contribution.

- **Catherine Bradshaw, PhD**
  Assistant Professor, Department of Mental Health, Associate Director, Johns Hopkins Center for the Prevention of Youth Violence, Johns Hopkins Bloomberg School of Public Health

- **Robert Crosnoe, PhD**
  Associate Professor, Department of Sociology & Population Research Center, University of Texas at Austin

- **Jacinda Dariotis, PhD**
  Assistant Scientist, Center for Adolescent Health, Department of Population, Family & Reproductive Health, Johns Hopkins Bloomberg School of Public Health

- **Nikeea C. Linder, PhD, MPH**
  Assistant Professor, Division of General Pediatrics & Adolescent Medicine, Department of Pediatrics & Department of Population, Family & Reproductive Health, Johns Hopkins School of Medicine & Bloomberg School of Public Health

- **Arik V. Marcell, MD, MPH**
  Assistant Professor, Division of General Pediatrics & Adolescent Medicine, Department of Pediatrics & Department of Population, Family & Reproductive Health, Johns Hopkins School of Medicine & Bloomberg School of Public Health

- **Sara Johnson, MPH, PhD**
  Assistant Professor, Department of Population, Family & Reproductive Health, Johns Hopkins Bloomberg School of Public Health

- **Lisa Pearce, PhD**
  Associate Professor, Department of Sociology, Fellow, Carolina Population Center, University of North Carolina at Chapel Hill

- **Stephen T. Russell, PhD**
  Professor & Director, Frances McClelland Institute for Children, Youth & Families, Norton School of Family & Consumer Sciences, University of Arizona

- **Freya L. Sonenstein, PhD**
  Director, Center for Adolescent Health, Professor, Department of Population, Family & Reproductive Health, Johns Hopkins Bloomberg School of Public Health

- **Janis Whitlock, MPH, PhD**
  Director, Cornell Research Program on Self-Injurious Behavior, Research Scientist, Family Life Development Center, Lecturer, Human Development Department, Cornell University

Members of the Adolescent Colloquium

The Adolescent Colloquium was formed as a partnership with the Center for Adolescent Health in 2005 to provide important contributions to the shaping of this project. We thank them for their dedication and participation.

- **Rebkha Atnafou, MPH**
  Executive Director, The After-School Institute

- **Robert Blum, MD, MPH, PhD**
  Director, Urban Health Institute, William H. Gates, Sr. Professor & Chair, Department of Population, Family & Reproductive Health, Johns Hopkins Bloomberg School of Public Health

- **Jean-Michel Brevelle**
  Sexual Minorities Program Manager, Maryland AIDS Administration

- **Peter R. Cohen, MD**
  Medical Director, Alcohol & Drug Abuse Administration, Maryland Department of Health & Mental Hygiene

- **Barbara Conrad, BSN, MPH**
  Chief, Division of Sexually Transmitted Diseases/HIV Partner Notification, Maryland Department of Health & Mental Hygiene

- **Cheryl De Pinto, MD, MPH**
  Medical Director, Child, Adolescent, & School Health, Center for Maternal & Child Health, Maryland Department of Health & Mental Hygiene

- **Christine Evans**
  Community Health Educator, Center for Maternal & Child Health, Maryland Department of Health & Mental Hygiene

- **Marina Finnegan, MHC**
  Director of Prevention Strategies, Governor's Office for Children, Maryland

- **Patricia I. Jones, BS**
  Abstinence Education Coordinator, Center for Maternal & Child Health, Maryland Department of Health & Mental Hygiene

- **Mary Anne Kane-Breschi**
  Office for Genetics & Children with Special Health Care Needs Resource Development, Maryland Department of Health & Mental Hygiene

- **Rebekah Lin**
  Communications & Technical Assistance Specialist, The After-School Institute

- **Pam Putman, BSN, MPH**
  Healthy Teens & Young Adults Family Planning & Reproductive Health, Maryland Department of Health & Mental Hygiene

- **Ilene Sparber, LCSW-C**
  Interagency Coalition on Teen Pregnancy & Parenting, Montgomery County Department of Health & Human Services

- **Mischa Toland**
  Interagency Coalition on Teen Pregnancy & Parenting, Montgomery County Department of Health & Human Services

- **Carmi Washington-Flood**
  Chief, Office of Community Relations & Initiatives, Maryland Department of Health & Mental Hygiene

- **Pearl Whitehurst**
  Program Coordinator, Office of Community Relations & Initiatives, Maryland Department of Health & Mental Hygiene

Additional Thanks

Denise Dalton, David Jernigan, PhD, Meg Tucker, Seante Hatcher, Beth Marshall, Rosemary Hutzler, Ann Stiller

We would like to thank the youth who contributed their voices, which can be found throughout the Guide.

Special thanks to Layne Humphrey and Christine Verdun Schoennberger for their dedication and hard work on the early version of the Guide.

Disclaimer: While many people have provided guidance in the development of this book, _The Teen Years Explained: A Guide to Healthy Adolescent Development_ represents the thoughts of its authors, who are responsible for its content. It does not reflect the views of the Adolescent Colloquium, the Scientific Advisory Board, the State of Maryland government agencies, Johns Hopkins University, nor any of its funders.

by Nicole Yohalem and Karen Pittman, Forum for Youth Investment

Not since the 2002 publication of *Community Programs to Promote Youth Development* have we recommended adding any lengthy publications to the "must-read" list for youth workers, teachers, parents, or anyone interested in ensuring young people's positive development. But make room on the bookshelf, because the time has come with the release of *The Teen Years Explained: A Guide to Healthy Adolescent Development.*

By compiling in plain English the science behind adolescence, the authors have produced a comprehensive yet accessible resource that 1) explains, without oversimplifying, the complex processes of development; 2) challenges and empowers adults to invest more attention, more time, and more resources in adolescents as they transition to adulthood; and 3) gives youth-development professionals the knowledge they need to ensure that healthy adolescent development is an explicit goal of their work.

Everything from basic social development theory to cutting-edge neuroscience is packed into this guide, making it a useful reminder of some key principles underlying the youth development movement and a resource for adults who find themselves helping teens navigate a world that likely feels different from the one they grew up in.

At the Forum for Youth Investment, we are committed to supporting leaders who are working on youth issues. One thing we try to do is meet people where they are, but quickly help them see a bolder path. Simple catchphrases often help us do that, and three in particular are reinforced by this guide.

1. Problem-free isn't fully prepared

In the 1990s, this phrase helped capture both the need for, and approaches to, risk reduction. Ensuring teenagers enter adulthood addiction-free, without dropping out of school, and with no arrest record is a short-sighted goal that reflects low expectations. Embracing adolescence as a time of opportunity is difficult, given the real risks associated with this period and the unacceptable numbers of young people who are, in fact, dangerously disconnected. Yet reframing development as a positive, normative process is critical if parents, professionals, and institutions are to support, socialize, challenge, and instruct.[i]

Without going into detail on effective practice, the Guide reinforces the idea that successful efforts to prevent specific problems and promote positive development depend on supportive relationships, accurate information, and skill-building opportunities.[ii]

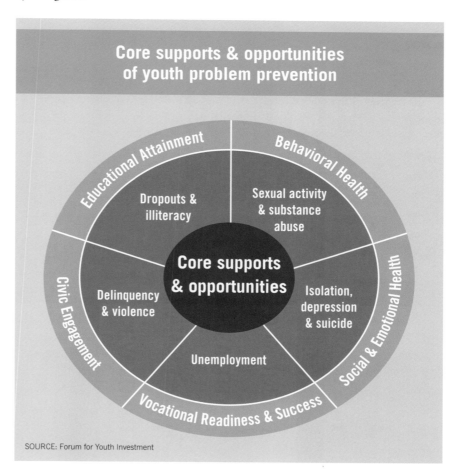

Core supports & opportunities of youth problem prevention

Educational Attainment

Behavioral Health

Dropouts & illiteracy

Sexual activity & substance abuse

Core supports & opportunities

Civic Engagement

Delinquency & violence

Isolation, depression & suicide

Social & Emotional Health

Unemployment

Vocational Readiness & Success

SOURCE: Forum for Youth Investment

Youth workers and youth organizations have long claimed some of the outcome areas depicted in the figure (e.g., social and emotional health, civic engagement, and behavioral health) and are increasingly being pressured to take on others (e.g., academics and physical health). The scientific evidence now firmly supports the notion that, while development unfolds across different domains, developmental processes are inextricably intertwined. Like it or not, youth work is an interdisciplinary endeavor. Behavioral health affects learning; cognitive development affects behavioral health; civic engagement influences identity development.

By describing and knitting together the processes that unfold across developmental domains and coming back to themes such as the importance of positive relationships, the Guide reminds readers that effective practitioners—whether employed in after-school programs, teen centers, schools, courts, camps, or hospitals—understand the basics of adolescent development and its implications for creating supportive learning environments where teens can thrive.

2. Young people don't grow up in programs, they grow up in communities

Gracefully avoiding a scientific debate about the role of nature vs. nurture, the Guide illustrates that development is both an individual process and one that is significantly influenced by the formal and informal contexts in which it unfolds.

Young people move in and out of numerous settings every day—familial, institutional, informal, virtual. The range of environments they encounter grows with the increasing autonomy of adolescence. Each of these represents an opportunity for development, derailment, or both. Cognitive development doesn't stop when the school bell rings, and social development doesn't kick in upon arrival at the teen center.

The Guide challenges us to remember that while we will not and should not always have control over adolescents, we can, in fact, shape many of the settings where they spend time. Creating contexts that nurture growth and minimize risk requires the kind of working knowledge of adolescent development that this guide offers.

3. We need youth-centered, not system-centered, approaches

The vast majority of policy and practice conversations about youth well-being taking place across the country focuses on *systems*. How can the juvenile justice system better prevent youth crime? How can we improve the school system to increase student engagement? Increasingly, conversations are taking place across multiple systems: How can juvenile justice and child welfare work together better to support transitioning youth? How can schools and community-based organizations work together to reduce the dropout rate?

While these attempts to work across systems are promising, most are still *system*-centered conversations. As a result, they are organized around and constrained by expertise and assumptions about systems, as opposed to expertise and assumptions about young people and their developmental needs. This is a *youth*-centered guide. Adolescence is described in its full complexity, yet in accessible terms.

Over the years, the Forum for Youth Investment has moved away from leading with terms like "adolescent development" and "youth development." We found that decision-makers are simply more interested in outcome than process, especially when it comes to teens and young adults. Stating that we wanted to help leaders leverage the considerable financial and human resources spent addressing specific problems (e.g., teen pregnancies, high school dropouts, and violence), we articulated a simple goal: to ensure that all young people are "ready by 21"—ready for college, work, and life.

If we are serious about changing the odds for young people—about ensuring that they are indeed ready for college, work, and life—then it is our responsibility as practitioners, advocates, and policy-makers to use the information in this guide to check our assumptions, allocate our resources, and rethink our approaches. This guide is a welcome and essential tool for every adult who has contact with young people. It helps makes us ready to help them be ready.

[i]Pittman, K., Irby, M., Tolman, J., Yohalem, N., & Ferber, T. (2003). *Preventing Problems, Promoting Development, Encouraging Engagement: Competing Priorities or Inseparable Goals?* Available online at www.forumfyi.org.

[ii]Forum for Youth Investment. (2005, May/June). What's Health Got to Do With It? *Forum Focus*, 3(2). Washington, DC: Forum for Youth Investment, Impact Strategies, Inc. Available online at www.forumfyi.org.

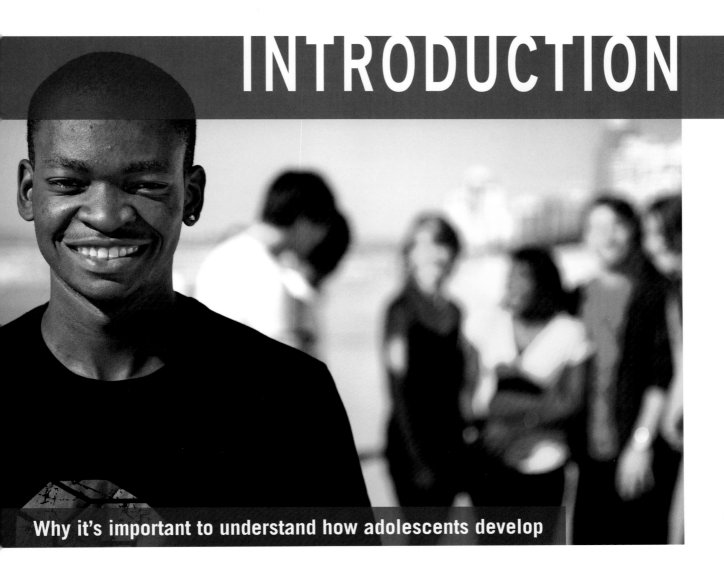

INTRODUCTION

Why it's important to understand how adolescents develop

The purpose of this guide is to serve as an essential resource for people who work with young people and for youth-serving organizations.

At no other time except infancy do human beings pack so much development into such a short period. During adolescence, children gain 50 percent of their adult body weight, become capable of reproducing, and experience an astounding transformation in their brains. All these changes occur in the context of—and indeed, allow for—rapidly expanding social spheres. Teens start assuming adult responsibilities such as finding a job, figuring out romantic relationships, and learning how to be a good friend.

Understanding these changes—developmentally, what is happening and why—can help both adults and teens enjoy the second decade of life. Knowledge of adolescent development empowers people who work with young people to advance teens' development. And it allows us all to sustain appreciation and compassion for the joys and aggravations of adolescence: the ebullience, the insecurities, the risk-taking, and the stunning growth in competence.

Healthy adolescent development

Most books on adolescence highlight the problems teens face and how adults can help resolve them. Missing from the plethora of resources focused on surviving adolescence is a description of what happens to the vast majority of young people: normal, healthy development. This guide is an attempt to fill that void. It describes the changes that happen during adolescence and how adults can promote healthy development.

This guide is based on several key ideas, all of which are supported by research evidence: 1) adolescence is a time of opportunity, not turmoil; 2) normal, healthy development is uneven; 3) young people develop positive attributes through learning and experience; and 4) the larger community plays a fundamental and essential role in helping young people move successfully into adulthood.

Adolescence is a time of opportunity, not turmoil

Research shows that adolescence —contrary to views that predominate in our media and culture—is actually positive for both teens and adults. Most adolescents succeed in school, are attached to their families and their communities, and emerge from their teen years without experiencing serious problems such as substance abuse or involvement with violence. Although teens experience emotions intensely—a consequence of brain development— for most, the teen years are not filled with angst and confusion. Rather, they are a time of concentrated social, emotional, and cognitive development.

Normal, healthy development is uneven

Adolescence includes periods of rapid physical growth and the emergence of secondary sexual characteristics (e.g., breasts in girls and deeper voices in boys). Not visible are internal physiologic, cognitive, and emotional changes. Changes on these multiple

fronts do not always happen in sync. Physically and sexually, young people, especially girls, may mature by their mid-teens. Yet the process of transforming the relatively inefficient brain of the child into a leaner, more proficient adult brain may not be completed until age 25.

Adding even more complexity, this out-of-sync pattern of development may seem to be constantly changing. In early adolescence a young person may be behind physically and ahead emotionally. That pattern can reverse later on as growth spurts occur in different areas of development.

This unevenness of development calls for active support by caring

adults. Although they may look like adults—and, at times, want to be treated as adults—teens are still in a formative stage. This guide provides multiple strategies for supporting young people's development.

Young people develop positive attributes through learning and experience

Throughout this guide, the term *positive youth development* is used. Positive youth development is the understanding, based on research, that healthy development is best promoted by creating opportunities to develop a set of core assets, dubbed the 5 C's: competence, confidence,

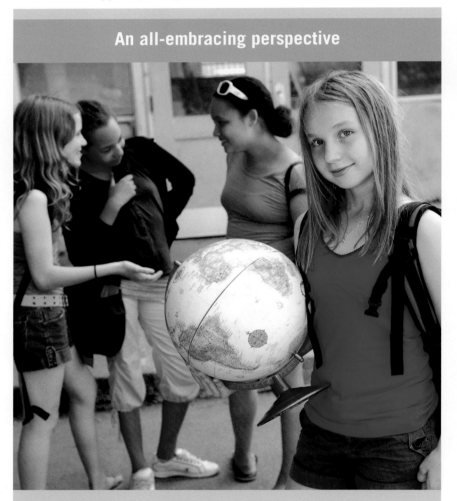

An all-embracing perspective

We use the term "adolescent" throughout *The Teen Years Explained: A Guide to Healthy Adolescent Development* to refer to all youth ages 10 to 19. It includes young people of all cultures and ethnicities, abilities and disabilities, as well as gays, lesbians, transgender and bisexual youth.

The 5 C's of positive youth development

Asset	Definition	How to Foster It
COMPETENCE	Perception that one has abilities and skills	Provide training and practice in specific skills, either academic or hands-on
CONFIDENCE	Internal sense of self efficacy and positive self-worth	Provide opportunities for young people to experience success when trying something new
CONNECTION	Positive bonds with people and institutions	Build relationships between youth and peers, teachers and parents
CHARACTER	A sense of right and wrong (morality), integrity, and respect for standards of correct behavior	Provide opportunities to practice increasing self-control and development of spirituality
CARING	A sense of sympathy and empathy for others	Care for young people

connection, character and caring (see above). Adolescents develop these core assets when they experience them in their own lives. A young person learns that he or she is good at something (competence) when given the opportunity to try and practice new things. Likewise, a young person learns to be caring by being cared for, and develops character by practicing self-control.

The positive youth development framework expands the traditional focus on reducing risks. Programs informed by the traditional framework—which remains important—tend to focus on avoiding bad things: drugs, unprotected sex, driving while drunk, or failing school. Although many risk-reduction strategies have been shown to be successful, research in the field of positive youth development has demonstrated that "problem-free is not fully prepared." Healthy adolescent development requires creating opportunities for adolescents to experience, learn, and practice the 5 C's. Examples

of effective strategies to promote healthy development are provided throughout this guide.

Community has a role: putting adolescence in context

Before the mid-1980s, adolescent research focused largely on development and behavior alone, looking at physical growth and how teens act. Little attention was paid to the settings in which children live. More recently, research has started to examine the contexts where adolescents develop. Context refers to the surroundings in which a child is growing up. The places where young people spend time—at home, with friends, in school, at work, in front of television, movies, or other media, or in the neighborhood—influence their development.

Research is starting to show a complex interaction between a young person and his or her context. People's surroundings and experiences can influence their emotional, cognitive,

and even physical development. At the same time, adolescents are not simply passive recipients of experience, all responding to developmental "inputs" in the same way. They interpret and respond to each new experience through the lenses of their innate personalities and prior experiences.

What does this mean for people who work with young people? It is essential to understand the strengths and needs of adolescents when designing programs or health-promotion strategies.

It is also important to consider the context or setting in which an adolescent lives, and to address the risks and assets of that environment.

How to use this guide

We designed this guide to be useful to the reader who has five minutes or five hours. Each chapter describes a different aspect of development—physical, cognitive, emotional and social, identity, sexual, and spiritual. The chapters do not need to be read in

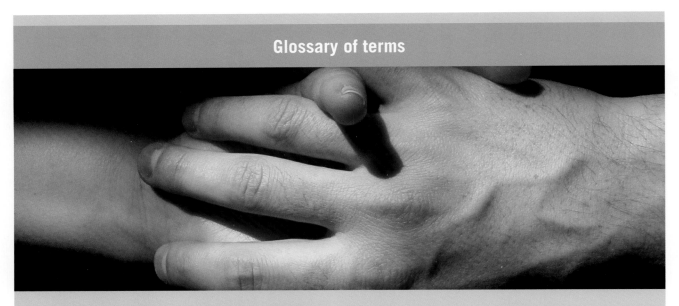

Glossary of terms

The Teen Years Explained: A Guide to Healthy Adolescent Development uses a few key terms throughout the chapters. Below are the definitions.

ADOLESCENCE Usually defined as the second decade of life, adolescence is the period of transition from childhood to adulthood. Researchers now note that bodily and brain changes associated with adolescence may begin as early as age 8 and extend until age 24.

HEALTH RISK BEHAVIORS These are behaviors that make one more likely to experience a negative health result. For example, unprotected sexual intercourse is a health risk behavior that makes one more susceptible to sexually transmitted infections and unplanned pregnancy. Health risk behaviors are commonly referred to as risky health behaviors.

POSITIVE YOUTH DEVELOPMENT Positive youth development is a framework for developing strategies and programs to promote healthy development. It emphasizes fostering positive developmental outcomes by providing young people the experiences and opportunities to develop core developmental assets. The list of core developmental assets typically includes what are known as the 5 C's: competence, connection, character, confidence, and caring.

PROTECTIVE FACTORS These are characteristics or behaviors that increase the likelihood of experiencing a positive result (e.g., the presence of a caring adult is a protective factor for school success). Protective factors directly promote healthy development and also reduce the negative impact of risk factors. Protective factors exist wherever one finds young people—in school, at home, and in the community—and include things such as a long-term relationship with a caring adult, opportunities to build skills and become good at something, and belonging to a group of friends who value academic achievement. Protective factors can also be internal to a person, such as having a sunny temperament.

PUBERTY The World Health Organization defines puberty as "the period in life when a child experiences physical, hormonal, sexual, and social changes and becomes capable of reproduction." It is associated with rapid growth and the appearance of secondary sexual characteristics. Puberty typically starts for girls between ages 8 and 13, and for boys between ages 9 and 14, and may continue until age 19 or older.

RISK FACTORS These are characteristics or behaviors that increase the likelihood of experiencing a negative result. For example, smoking is a risk factor for developing heart disease, and harsh parenting a risk factor for depression. Like protective factors, risk factors can be innate (e.g., having a genetic vulnerability to a disease), environmental (e.g., being exposed to lead or living in a dangerous neighborhood), or learned behaviors (e.g., not wearing seatbelts).

sequence, as adolescent development does not happen in sequence. The last chapter puts the various dimensions of development together in a single package and returns to the theme of development happening at different rates.

Within each chapter are tips for how to promote healthy adolescent development. These, too, can be read by themselves. Finally, throughout the guide we have two- and three-page descriptions of issues that young people and people who work with young

people have told us are of concern to them. These include, among others, obesity and nutrition, stress, bullying, and the effects of drugs and alcohol on the teen brain.

PHYSICAL DEVELOPMENT

CHAPTER 1

Puberty—timing differs from teen to teen

"I have a good body image. If you don't have a good body image, then you will push and push yourself until you think you are perfect." *Girl, 12*

Physical changes are perhaps the most noticeable signs that a child is becoming an adolescent. The physical transformations of puberty affect every aspect of the lives of teens. Changing bodies may lead to changes in circles of peers, adults' view of teens, and teens' view of themselves.

Great variability can be found in the time of onset of puberty, defined broadly as the biological and physical changes that occur during adolescence and result in the capacity to reproduce.

For girls, puberty can start as early as eight years old. Girls experience a rapid growth spurt, typically starting around age 10. This growth spurt lasts for a few years, and then girls continue to grow more slowly until they are 17 or 18. During puberty, breast buds develop, pubic hair appears, height increases, menstruation begins, and hips widen.

Boys usually begin their growth spurt one to two years after most girls. They continue to develop for three to four years after the girls, which means boys may not finish growing physically until they are 21. For boys, pubic hair appears, the penis gets longer, height increases, the voice deepens, and muscle mass develops.

Puberty is triggered by the actions of hormones on various parts of the body. New hormones might be at work for several months before development becomes outwardly evident. For adolescent boys, in fact, the visible changes come late in the development process.

From the teen's perspective, puberty puts a bright spotlight on body image. Body image is the picture of personal physical appearance that people hold in their minds. It is the concept of one's own changing body—how it feels, how it moves through space, how it looks in the mirror, and how one thinks it looks to others. Body image can be shaped by emotions, perceptions, physical sensations, experience, and moods. It can also be powerfully influenced by cultural messages and societal standards.

Why do I look so different from my friends?

Some teenagers start maturing early, while others are late bloomers. As a result, young people may look out-of-sync developmentally with their peers. Adolescents may experience a lot of uncertainty when they do not look similar to other young people their age.

For example, one girl may be six months younger than her BFF (Best Friend Forever), yet start menstruating and wearing a bra first. Some boys may look in the mirror and moan that they are freaks because their nose and ears have suddenly grown too big for their

BRAIN BOX

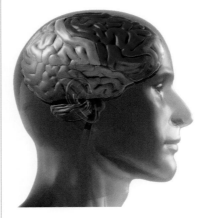

Recent studies using MRI analysis indicate that a wave of overproduction of gray matter—the thinking part of the brain—occurs just prior to puberty. This thickening of gray matter peaks at around age 11 in girls and 12 in boys, after which the gray matter actually thins somewhat. Previously it was thought that the brain's wiring underwent just one bout of "pruning" that was finished by the age of 3, but researchers now have discovered that structural changes occur in adolescence and that teens' gray matter waxes and wanes in different functional brain areas at different times in development. Brain development continues up to age 25.

SOURCE: Giedd, JN, Blumenthal, J, Jeffries, NO, Castellanos, FX, Liu H; Zijdenbos, A, et al. (1999). Brain development during childhood and adolescence: a longitudinal MRI study. *Nature Neuroscience*, 2(10), 861-3.

faces. And they may be right, at least about the change in proportion, since facial features develop at different rates, as do hands and feet.

The timing of physical and cognitive changes varies throughout adolescence. Even if a teenager is adult-sized, he or she may not be fully developed emotionally or cognitively. Conversely, a young person may not look full-grown, but could possess more advanced reasoning and abstract thinking skills than his or her more physically developed peers.

Challenges to early and late development

Early development for girls and late development for boys present the greatest challenges to healthy body image. For girls, puberty brings on characteristics often seen as less than ideal—roundness and an increase in body fat around the hips and thighs. Conversely, the masculine ideal is often measured by increased size and broadness, which makes delayed development tough for boys.

Although girls may begin experiencing physical changes earlier than boys, they may not be developed enough cognitively or skilled enough socially to handle the way they are treated now that they have a rapidly maturing body. Signs of puberty in females—specifically, breast development

Helping teens during puberty

- Familiarize teens with the facts about biology and reproduction. Experts recommend discussing puberty with children starting at age 8 or 9—or even as early as 5 or 6, depending on the curiosity and the maturity level of the child—so they are prepared for changes when they occur.
- Take comments about appearance seriously and spend time actively listening to such concerns.
- Get teens to talk about their feelings, fears, and what stresses them out about

the physical changes happening in their bodies.
- When teens talk about their feelings, listen. Do not jump in too quickly with advice or, worse, tell them their feelings are irrational or unfounded.
- Encourage early-developers to stay away from older peer groups and help connect them to peers their own age.
- Understand that although a teen may appear physically mature, he or she is not an adult and cannot be expected to think or act as an adult.

and menstruation—are associated with the end of childhood and a change in social status. Girls with fuller breasts and body shapes may be particularly vulnerable to unwanted attention from boys and older males. They may feel pressure to develop sexual identities and pursue sexual relationships, even though they do not feel prepared.

Helping an early-developing girl navigate these stresses often depends on the unique aspects of her culture or surroundings. Cultural differences may also exist with respect to ideals of body type, shape, and size.

Girls who are obese or overweight are much more likely to develop early and experience early menstruation, defined as beginning before age 11. This is especially true if they have been overweight throughout childhood. The combination of extra pounds, early development, and early menstruation can be distressing, since these girls have to deal with both a mature body and entrenched stigmas about excess weight encountered at home, at school, in the media, and out in the community.

In boys, puberty can bring on traits the culture perceives as admirable—height, broadness, strength, speed, muscularity. Early development in boys has some social benefits, since added height and muscular appearance may result in increased popularity and confidence.

However, stress and anxiety from physical changes during puberty also are typical for early-developing boys. They may be pushed to have sex before they are not ready, or receive unwanted sexual advances they cannot handle emotionally. Teens often have a strong need to feel accepted, so they may

NORMAL PHYSICAL GROWTH

Girls

Boys

Girls

- Appearance of breast buds (between 8 and 12 years of age), followed by breast development (13-18)

- Development of pubic hair (11-14)

- Growth spurt begins (average age, 10), which adds inches to height and hip circumference

- Menses begins (average age, 12, normal age range between 9 and 16)

- Enlargement of ovaries, uterus, labia, and clitoris; thickening of the endo-metrium and vaginal mucosa

- Appearance of underarm hair (13-16)

- Dental changes, which include jaw growth and development of molars

- Development of body odor and acne

Boys

- Testicular enlargement, beginning as early as 9-½ years of age
- Appearance of pubic hair (10-15)
- Onset of spermarche, or sperm found in the ejaculate
- Lengthening of genitals (11-14)
- Rapid enlargement of the larynx, pharynx, and lungs, which can lead to alterations in vocal quality (i.e., voice cracking)
- Changes in physical growth (average age, 14), first seen in the hands and feet, followed by the arms and legs, and then the trunk and chest
- Weight gain and increases in lean body mass and muscle mass (11-16)
- Doubling of heart size and vital lung capacity, increase in blood pressure and blood volume
- Growth of facial and body hair, which may not be completed until the mid-20s
- Dental changes, which include jaw growth and development of molars
- Development of body odor and acne

Potential unhealthy responses to physical changes

It is normal for young people to feel self-conscious and fret about their appearance. Once in a while, more serious difficulties arise as teens deal with physical changes. These include:

- Fear, confusion, or withdrawal, especially during early adolescence, ages 10-14
- Obsessive concern about appearance
- Excessive dieting or exercise
- Early-maturing teens being exposed to social situations they may not be ready to handle (e.g., being invited to parties with older teens)
- Experiencing depression and eating disorders
- Being bullied, teased, or excluded

be ill-prepared to defend themselves against unwelcome sexual attention.

Early-developing adolescents are also more vulnerable to making risky decisions because their physical and brain changes are happening on widely divergent tracks. Their physical development may garner invitations and opportunities with older teens and young adults (parties, drinking, etc.) just as changes in the brain trigger the desire for thrill-seeking and risk-taking. However, their brains are not fully developed, so the urge to experiment is not balanced by the capacity to make sound judgments.

Pubertal development at later ages is completely normal, but boys and girls with delayed physical maturity may see themselves—or friends and family may see them—as still stuck in childhood.

Later developers, especially boys, can be excluded from sports. They might be bullied and picked on, which puts them at risk for low self-esteem and depression.

When puberty is not on track

While there is no set schedule for physical changes, on average girls

begin puberty with the development of breast buds around the age of 10, with growth spurts and menstruation usually following two years later. For boys, testicular enlargement, growth spurts, and other signs of puberty normally start at 12 or 13—although some pubertal changes can begin at the age of 9. The rate of maturity may be rapid for some adolescents, while others may take four or five years to complete their development. When a child begins to develop much earlier than usual, it is called *precocious puberty*. Precocious puberty in boys is defined as testicular or penile enlargement, and genital or body and facial hair growth occurring before the age of 9. In girls, it is breast

> "The best thing about my looks is my eyes and lips. The things I like the least are my butt, hips, and thighs."
>
> *Girl, 15*

development, onset of menstruation, and pubic or underarm hair growth at the age of 7 or 8.

It is generally thought that improved nutrition has resulted in the earlier start of puberty throughout the 20th century, although genetic, metabolic, and environmental factors also contribute.

Physical growth much later than average—for example, in girls who have not developed breast buds by age 13 and in boys whose testicles have not enlarged by age 13-½—is termed *delayed puberty*. The causes of delayed puberty may be growth patterns within the family, medical conditions, eating disorders, problems with the pituitary or thyroid glands, or chromosome irregularities. Girls who are extremely

Eating disorders

Boys, as well as girls, can develop eating disorders, which are accompanied by severely distorted views of their bodies.

ANOREXIA NERVOSA Extreme weight loss and a fear of weight gain. Warning signs include dramatic weight loss, preoccupation with weight, food, calories, fat grams or dieting, excessive or obsessive exercise, and frequent comments about feeling overweight despite extreme weight loss.

BULIMIA NERVOSA Bulimics eat large amounts of food and then vomit or take excessive amounts of laxatives to lose weight. Warning signs include evidence of binge-eating or vomiting (purging), excessive or obsessive exercise, and ritual behavior that accompanies binging and purging sessions.

BODY DYSMORPHIC DISORDER An intense preoccupation with a perceived defect in one's appearance.

MUSCLE DYSMORPHIA Sometimes known as "reverse anorexia," muscle dysmorphia is a preoccupation with the idea that one's body is not sufficiently lean and muscular. Warning signs include working out and weight-lifting to the point where school, social life, and family life are pushed aside. Boys are most susceptible to muscle dysmorphia, and often in adolescents it leads to such dangerous behavior as steroid use.

active in sports may experience delayed puberty because their level of exercise keeps them quite lean, and girls need a certain amount of fat in order to start their periods.

Weight and height measurements may also indicate that an adolescent's development is off-track. Excess weight is associated with earlier onset of menstruation in girls. Teenagers who are short for their age are usually physically normal, but short stature can also be caused by bone defects, systemic illness, and hormone deficiency. Similarly, extreme tallness can be normal, but it can also be associated with a syndrome or hormonal deficiency. Medical tests can evaluate whether or not these conditions exist, and a doctor can advise treatment options.

Physical changes & healthy body image

The way adolescents feel about their bodies can affect the way they feel about themselves as a whole.

Although most body image research has focused on white youth, research does indicate that African-American adolescents, particularly girls, tend to have healthier body images than their white counterparts. Asian Americans may have healthier body images than their white, African-American, and Hispanic peers.

Concerns about the body can erode the quality of life for young people, keeping them from healthy relationships, taking up an inordinate amount of time they could be using to cultivate other aspects of their personalities, and leading them to overspending on goods and services to improve their bodies.

Anabolic steroids and legal and illicit supplements (recombinant human growth hormone, injections of insulin to increase muscle mass, thyroxine, clenbuterol, cocaine) are used by athletes to boost strength and sports performance. Steroids are easily found on the Internet or in the locker room at some private gyms. Dietary supplements with similar chemical properties can be bought at health food stores. Young people who want steroids can find them.

Recent studies show that 3 percent to 9 percent of teenagers illegally use steroids, with the highest rates of use reported in the middle-school years.

Anabolic steroids are a group of laboratory-made drugs designed to mimic the effects of the male hormone testosterone. These drugs cause muscle and bone growth, as well as the development of male sexual characteristics. For girls, steroids can cause the development of male-pattern baldness, infertility, facial hair, and irreversible hoarseness of the voice.

Anabolic steroids can also increase estrogen production as the body tries to compensate for the high levels of male-dominant hormones. In boys, the increase in estrogen can cause hot flashes, testicular shrinkage, weight gain, bloating, and the growth of fatty breast tissue.

If teenagers abuse steroids before the normal puberty growth spurt is complete, they may never reach their full adult height. Humans are programmed to stop developing after puberty, and steroid use can boost hormone levels to the point where the body is tricked into thinking growth is done.

Some of the short-term side effects of anabolic steroids for both boys and girls include acne, hostility, anxiety, and aggression. The psychological effects of steroid use can be severe, and include paranoia, delusions or hallucinations, depression, and suicidal thoughts. Steroid use also can lead to heart disease, and liver and prostate cancer.

Signs of steroid use include quick weight and muscle gains, combativeness and rage (known as "'roid rage"), jaundice, purple or red spots on the body, swelling of feet and lower legs, trembling, persistent unpleasant breath odor, severe acne and oily skin.

Dealing with powerful media images of youth

- Explain that media images do not reflect the average person—there is wide diversity in physical appearance and rate of development.

- Point out how body sizes, shapes, and faces are altered in magazines and photographs using software programs like Photoshop. Waists and thighs are whittled, cheekbones sharpened and lips plumped for women. Muscles are pumped up and defined, and complexions smoothed for men.

- Encourage critical thinking about the media and the nature of our consumer culture. Now is the perfect time to help teens develop their critical thinking skills—help them question what is "normal."

- Turn to resources that reflect realistic, diverse appearances of actual people.

- Encourage activities that focus on attributes other than physical appearance, such as academics, sports, music, the arts, writing, or crafts.

- Reinforce these messages regularly.

To cultivate a healthy body image, adolescents can tap into their developing critical thinking skills. A healthy dose of skepticism can help them sift through the bombardment of messages related to body image, appearance, attractiveness, and eating that they encounter in the media, at home, and from their friends.

Adults can provide accurate information regarding physical development, healthy eating, and the effects of media, society, culture, peers, and family on body image. Beginning at a young age, adolescents need to understand that bodies come in all shapes and sizes and that these disparities are nothing out of the ordinary.

13 is not a magic number

There is no single age at which teens enter puberty. Thirteen is not the miraculous age when a child suddenly transforms into a young adult. Puberty can begin as early as age 8 or as late as 15. Regardless of when a child enters puberty, the changes he or she undergoes affect his or her social interactions and psychological outlook.

Adults should be aware of these changes and of the way cultural differences play into such issues as sexual maturity, body image, and pressures to behave like a fully grown man or woman.

> ## "I look at photos in magazines and on TV and no way do I measure up."
> *Girl, 14*

KEY FEATURES IN ADOLESCENT GROWTH AND DEVELOPMENT

AGES	PHYSICAL	EMOTIONAL
10-14 	• Body fat increases (girls) • Breasts begin to enlarge (girls) • Menstrual periods begin (girls) • Hips widen (girls) • Testicles and penis grow larger (boys) • Voice deepens (boys) • Breasts can get tender (girls and boys) • Height and weight increases (girls and boys) • Skin and hair become oilier, pimples may appear (girls and boys) • Appetite may increase (girls and boys) • Body hair grows (girls and boys) • Hormonal levels change (girls and boys) • Brain develops (girls and boys)	• Sense of identity develops • May feel awkward or strange about themselves and their bodies • Focus on self increases • Ability to use speech to express feelings improves • Close friendships gain importance • Realization grows that parents are not perfect, have faults • Overt affection toward parents declines • Occasional rudeness with parents occurs • Complaints that parents interfere with independence increase • Friends and peers influence clothing styles and interests • Childish behavior may return, particularly at times of stress
15-19 	• Girls usually reach full physical development • Boys reach close to full physical development • Voice continues to lower (boys) • Facial hair appears (boys) • Weight and height gain continue (boys) • Eating habits can become sporadic—skipping meals, late-night eating (girls and boys)	• Independent functioning increases • Firmer and more cohesive sense of personal identity develops • Examination of inner experiences becomes more important and may include writing a blog or diary • Ability for delayed gratification and compromise increases • Ability to think ideas through increases • Engagement with parents declines • Peer relationships remain important • Emotional steadiness increases • Social networks expand and new friendships are formed • Concern for others increases

COGNITIVE	SEXUAL	MORAL/VALUES
• Interests tend to focus on the present, thoughts of the future are limited	• Girls develop ahead of boys	• Testing of rules and limits increases
• Intellectual interests expand and gain in importance	• Shyness, blushing, and modesty increases	• More consistent evidence of conscience becomes apparent
• Ability to do work (physical, mental, emotional) expands	• Showing off may increase	• Capacity for abstract thought develops
• Capacity for abstract thinking increases	• Interest in privacy increases	• Ideals develop, including selection of role models
• Risk-taking behaviors may emerge (experimenting with tobacco, alcohol, physical risks)	• Interest in sex increases	• Questioning of moral rights and privileges increases
	• Exploration of issues and questions about sexuality and sexual orientation begins	
	• Concerns about physical and sexual attractiveness to others may develop	
	• Worries about being "normal" become common	
	• Short-term romantic relationships may occur	
• Interests focus on near-future and future	• Feelings of love and passion intensify	• Interest in moral reasoning increases
• More importance is placed on goals, ambitions, role in life	• More serious relationships develop	• Interest in social, cultural, and family traditions expands
• Capacity for setting goals and following through increases	• Sharing of tenderness and fears with romantic partner increases	• Emphasis on personal dignity and self-esteem increases
• Work habits become more defined	• Sense of sexual identity becomes more solid	• Capacity increases for useful insight
• Planning capability expands	• Capacity for affection and sensual love increases	
• Ability for foresight grows		
• Risk-taking behaviors may emerge (experimenting with tobacco, drugs, alcohol, reckless driving)		

CHART SOURCES: Adapted from www.aacap.org/publications/factsfam/develop.htm. American Academy of Child and Adolescent Psychiatry, *Normal Adolescent Development*, handout, 2/2005; http://www.nlm.nih.gov/medlineplus/ency/article/02003.htm.

BRAINPAGE

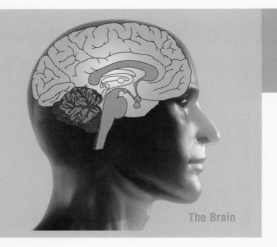

The Brain

In *The Teen Years Explained: A Guide to Healthy Adolescent Development*, you will find many references to the rich cognitive changes and development that occur throughout the teen years. This page will help explain the different parts of the brain and how they function.

The human brain is an extremely complex organ composed of interdependent parts, each with its own specific functions and properties. The brain has three fundamental segments: the forebrain, the midbrain, and the hindbrain.

The Forebrain

The **forebrain** is the most advanced and the largest section of the brain, located in its uppermost part. The forebrain is involved in all brain functions except for the autonomic activities of the brain stem. It is the part of the brain responsible for emotions, memory, and "higher-order" activities such as thinking and reasoning. The forebrain is made up of the cerebrum and the limbic system.

The cerebrum, or cerebral cortex, is divided into two hemispheres (left and right). Each hemisphere consists of four sections, called lobes:

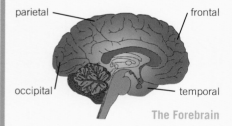

The Forebrain

- **Occipital Lobe**—Located at the back of the head just above the cerebellum, the occipital lobe processes sensory information from the eyes.
- **Temporal Lobe**—Located at the sides of the head above the ears, the temporal lobes perform several functions, including speech, perception and some types of memory.
- **Parietal Lobe**—Located at the top of the head, the parietal lobe receives data from the skin, including heat, cold, pressure, pain, and how the body is positioned in space.
- **Frontal Lobe**—Located under the forehead, the frontal lobe controls reasoning, planning, voluntary movement, and some aspects of speech. The prefrontal cortex is the part of the frontal lobe right behind the forehead. It is associated with complex cognitive skills such as being able to differentiate among conflicting thoughts, determine good and bad, identify future consequences of current activities, and suppress impulses. As the adolescent brain develops, the prefrontal cortex becomes increasingly connected with the seat of emotions, the limbic system, allowing reason and emotion to be better coordinated. The prefrontal cortex has also been linked to personality.

The limbic system, the set of brain structures that form the inside border of the cerebrum, accounts for about one-fifth of the brain's volume. The limbic system serves three functions: First, in cooperation with the brain stem, it regulates temperature, blood pressure, heart rate, and blood sugar. Second, two parts of the limbic system, the hippocampus and the amygdala, are essential to forming memories. Third, the limbic system is the center of human emotions. The amygdala is thought to link emotions with sensory inputs from the environment. Nerve impulses to the amygdala trigger the emotions of rage, fear, aggression, reward, and sexual attraction. These emotions trigger the action of the hypothalamus, which regulates blood pressure and body temperature.

The Midbrain

The **midbrain** is the topmost section of the brain stem and the smallest region of the brain. It is associated with some, but not all, reflex actions, as well as with eye movements and hearing.

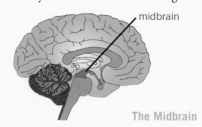

The Midbrain

The midbrain also contains several structures necessary for voluntary movement.

The Hindbrain

The **hindbrain** is the part located at the upper section of the spinal cord. The hindbrain includes the brain stem and the cerebellum. The brain stem, sometimes called the "reptilian brain," is the most basic area of the brain and controls breathing, heartbeat, and digestion. Next to the brain stem is the cerebellum, which is responsible for many learned physical skills, such as posture, balance, and coordination. Actions such as throwing a baseball or using a keyboard take thought and effort at first, but become more natural with practice because the memory of how to do them is stored in the cerebellum.

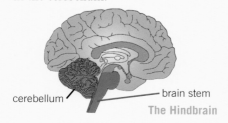

The Hindbrain

Obesity: Nutrition and Exercise

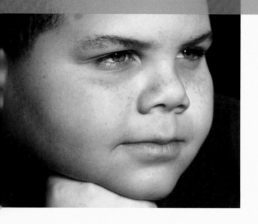

Obesity is a societal problem

Weight matters

Many young people today are living large. Obesity rates have doubled since 1980 among children and have tripled for adolescents. In the past 20 years, the proportion of adolescents aged 12 to 19 who are obese increased from 5 percent to 18 percent. Obesity is defined as a body mass index (BMI) that is equal to or greater than the 95th percentile for age and gender on growth charts developed by the Centers for Disease Control and Prevention (CDC).

A predisposition to obesity can be inherited. However, genetic factors do not explain the dramatic increase in obesity over the last 30 years. Human beings, like animals, are hardwired to eat not simply to sustain life, but to eat high-calorie foods in anticipation of an unpredictable food supply. Our surroundings make it possible to eat fatty foods on a regular basis, but difficult to burn off all those calories through activity. High-fat food is cheap and tasty, and teens' primary activities—school and media consumption—are sedentary.

Thus, obesity is a social problem rather than a personal flaw or a failure of willpower. Teens, especially, are impacted by their surroundings, and

THE PERILS OF POUNDS

Being overweight or obese is more than a matter of appearance. Excess pounds contribute significantly to health problems and can lead to Type 2 (adult-onset) diabetes, high blood pressure, stroke, heart conditions, cancer, gallstones and gall bladder disease, bone and joint problems, sleep apnea, and breathing difficulties. An adolescent who is obese (with a body mass index above the 95th percentile) has a 60 percent chance of developing one of these conditions.

In addition, studies have found that overweight youth are at greater risk for emotional distress than their non-overweight peers. Overweight teenagers have fewer friends, are more likely to be socially isolated, and suffer higher rates of depression than young people of normal weight. Being overweight also affects self-esteem. According to one study, obese girls aged 13 to 14 are four times more likely to suffer from low self-esteem than non-obese girls. Low self-esteem in adolescents is associated with higher rates of loneliness, sadness, and nervousness.

several studies at the University of Illinois-Chicago and the University of Michigan confirm that our modern environment is designed to make adolescents fat.

There are some environmental factors that contribute to teen obesity.

- Schools sell more high-fat, high-calorie foods and sugary drinks than nutritious, lower-calorie choices.
- Low-income communities offer limited access to healthy food. In some neighborhoods, convenience stores are the only places to buy food.
- Adolescents live sedentary lives. Teens spend the school day mostly sitting, and then go on to spend an average of three more hours parked in front of a TV or computer screen.
- School physical education programs have been slashed. In 1991, 42 percent of high school students participated in daily phys. ed. classes. By 2007, that number was 25 percent or lower.
- Airwaves are saturated with food-product ads. Teenagers see, on average, 17 ads a day for candy and snack foods, or more than 6,000 ads a year.
- Big portions provide far more calories than young people can burn up. Fast-food burgers can top

1,200 calories; 64-oz. sodas have become the norm; and some popular restaurant chains offer entrees that weigh in at 1,600 calories. The average adolescent needs only 2,300 to 2,500 calories a day.

Because the causes of excess weight are so complex, dietary changes are just one aspect of treating obesity. Adolescent weight problems can be related to poor eating habits, overeating or binging, physical inactivity, family history of obesity, stressful life events or changes (divorce, moves, deaths, and abuse), problems with family and friends, low self-esteem, depression, and other mental health conditions.

Teens are consuming more calories, but getting less nourishment

Adequate nutrition during adolescence is particularly important because of the rapid growth teenagers experience: they gain 50 percent of their adult weight and 50 percent of their bone mass during this decade of life.

Dietary choices and habits established during adolescence greatly influence future health. Yet many studies report that teens consume few fruits and vegetables and are not receiving the calcium, iron, vitamins, or minerals necessary for healthy development. Low-income youth are more susceptible to nutritional deficiencies, and since their diets tend to be made up of high-calorie and high-fat foods, they are also at greater risk for overweight or obesity.

Teasing about weight is toxic

Weight is one of the last sanctioned targets of prejudice left in society. Being overweight or obese subjects a teen to teasing and stigmatization by peers and adults. It can happen at home, at school, on the street—anywhere, even on TV. Ads and programming usually portray the overweight as the target of jokes, perpetual losers, and not as smart or successful as their thinner counterparts.

Teasing by family members, including parents, is surprisingly common, perhaps because family members mistakenly believe they are being helpful when they draw attention to someone's size or harass them about what they are eating. When they label their overweight adolescents with such epithets as "greedy," "lazy," or "little piggies," parents and siblings become an integral part of the problem.

A 2003 study of nearly 5,000 teenagers in the Minneapolis area found that 29 percent of girls and 16 percent of boys were teased by family

WAYS YOU CAN MAKE A
DIFFERENCE

- **REALIZE** that "kid-friendly" meals such as chicken nuggets, fries, and pizza with meat toppings are not the healthiest choices.

- **ADVOCATE** for recreation and com-munity centers and safe parks and trails so that youths can readily participate in physical activities and sports programs.

- **DISCOURAGE** late-night eating or the habit of consuming most of the day's calories in the evening.

- **RALLY** for the building of supermarkets and for greater access to fresh foods in urban neighborhoods.

- **PUSH** for direct access from bus and subway routes to farmers' markets.

- **SUPPORT** schoolwide efforts to promote physical activity and to limit offerings of junk foods and sugary beverages in the cafeteria and vending machines.

- **JOIN** forces with adolescents on an advocacy project insisting that food companies live up to their promises to stop marketing unhealthy foods to youth.

- **ACKNOWLEDGE** disparate views of the body and food based on gender, such as approval of larger size among boys.

- **EXAMINE** whether entrenched beliefs within your family, e.g., that it is important to finish everything on your plate, might be contributing to overeating.

members and one-third of the girls and one-fourth of the boys had been teased by their peers about their weight.

Weight-based taunting is not harmless. Adolescents in the study saw the teasing as having a greater negative impact on their self-image than did their actual body size.

Teasing should be taken seriously and never tolerated at home, in school, or in the community. Policies have helped to establish norms making ethnic slurs unacceptable. Perhaps similar policies can be formed to send a clear message that bullying people about body shape is not sanctioned in the schools or the community.

What can be done?
Young people can conquer weight problems and get adequate nutrition with a combination of a healthful diet, regular physical activity, counseling, and support from adults and peers.

For severely obese teens, medication or bariatric surgery is sometimes prescribed to supplement weight management efforts.

While proper diet and exercise improve physical health, parents and caregivers can also enhance mental health by emphasizing the overweight teen's strengths and positive qualities. After all, the measure of a young person's worth is far more than the numbers on the scale.

Some heavier adolescents will lose excess weight through positive lifestyle changes and through the normal growth spurts of puberty that make their bodies taller and leaner. In other cases, obesity becomes a life-long struggle.

Eating healthy foods in right-sized portions and exercising are lifelong habits, not temporary fixes. During growth spurts, adolescents do need a lot of calories, and the classic portrait

of a teenager as a bottomless pit—someone who can consume volumes of food and burn it all off—seems to hold true. These increased calories should come from healthy foods because teens need more nutrition as well as more calories. Learning to pay attention to cues of fullness from the body, as opposed to eating mindlessly, will help teens avoid a habit of overeating in later years when their metabolism inevitably slows down.

Adults can help control what happens in the home, schools, and neighborhood when it comes to eating and exercise. One of the best ways adults can influence young people is by changing their own eating and exercise habits. Adults can help young people establish healthy habits by

- Not skipping breakfast.
- Eating fruits, vegetables, lean protein, and whole grains.
- Cooking dinner at home using fresh, whole foods.
- Not buying or drinking beverages with added sugars.
- Building exercise and physical activity into one's own daily routines and encouraging one's children to join them.
- Not inappropriately encouraging youth to lose weight.

Weight gain accompanies puberty: teens grow in height, boys develop muscle mass; girls develop breasts and hips; and both boys and girls can put on body fat before a growth spurt. Adults should understand normal physical development (see the Physical Development chapter) to avoid putting undue pressure on an adolescent to be a certain size or weight.

"I think there's a lot of pressure out there to look perfect, but what's perfect?"
Girl, 16

COGNITIVE DEVELOPMENT

CHAPTER 2

The ever-expanding teenage brain

"I see and think differently now that I am a teenager. I know that there are negative and positive outcomes to everything that you do." *Girl, 14*

Newly developed thinking skills are one of the most thrilling aspects of adolescence. As their ability to think in abstract terms grows, young people love to debate, challenge established ideas or values, and question authority. They begin to question notions of absolute truth and to acquire the capability to present logical arguments.

This higher level of brainpower helps adolescents to consider the future, judge options, solve problems, and set goals. Part of gaining new thinking skills includes making mistakes and learning from them. Adults can play an important role in guiding cognitive development by helping young people master the skills of critical thinking and decision making.

The three main components of adolescent cognitive skills

In adolescence, cognitive development occurs in three main areas. First, young people strengthen their advanced reasoning skills, which includes thinking about multiple options and possibilities, pondering things hypothetically (the age-old "what if...?" questions), and following a logical thought process.

Second, teenagers start to develop abstract thinking skills, meaning they think about things that cannot be seen, heard, or touched. Abstract thought allows one to think about faith, love, trust, beliefs and spirituality, as well as higher mathematics.

Third, they enlarge their capacity to think about thinking, a process known as "meta-cognition." Meta-cognition allows young people to consider how they feel and what they are thinking, and also involves being able to think about how one is perceived by others. Meta-cognition can also be used to develop strategies such as mnemonic devices, which are useful in memorization and learning.

Recent neurological findings map changes in the teenage brain

The brains of babies and toddlers produce billions of brain cells (neurons) and connections between brain cells (synapses). Then, starting around age 3, the synapses are "pruned." Researchers have discovered a second period of overproduction of synapses that starts just before puberty (age 11 in girls, 12 in boys), also followed by pruning.

The pruning of synapses appears to be an essential part of brain maturation. Taking away the weaker synapses allows the remaining ones to become stronger and more stable, much like the pruning of a tree allows the remaining branches to thrive. Be-

BRAIN BOX

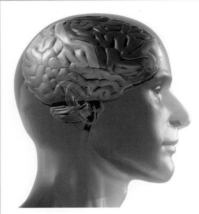

The teen years are a time of intense brain changes. Interestingly, two of the primary brain functions develop at different rates. Recent brain research indicates that the part of the brain that perceives rewards from risk, the limbic system, kicks into high gear in early adolescence. The part of the brain that controls impulses and engages in longer-term perspective, the frontal lobes, matures later. This may explain why teens in mid-adolescence take more risks than older teens. As the frontal lobes become more developed, two things happen. First, self-control develops as teens are better able to assess cause and effect. Second, more areas of the brain become involved in processing emotions, and teens become better at accurately interpreting others' emotions.

SOURCE: Steinberg, L. (2008) A social neuroscience perspective on adolescent risk-taking. *Developmental Review*, 28:78-106.

tween ages 13 and 18, adolescents lose approximately 1 percent of their gray matter every year.

The spurt of synapse formation and pruning during adolescence occurs in several parts of the brain, including the prefrontal cortex. The prefrontal cortex is responsible for advanced reasoning, including the ability to plan, understand cause and effect, think through scenarios, and manage impulses. There may be an important link between brain development and an adolescent's ability to stop to consider consequences, develop logical plans, or filter thoughts before blurting them out.

The brain changes continue up to at least age 21, and some scientists believe maturation is not complete until 25. Brain development seems to vary so much between individuals that it is impractical to pinpoint a specific age at which young people reach full maturity in thinking and reasoning. Throughout adolescence, the capacity for advanced reasoning, abstract thinking, and meta-cognition expands and improves.

Do brain changes spur risk-taking?

For decades, the story line for adolescents—written both by developmental psychologists and by parents—was that adolescents underestimate risk.

Teens, it was thought, feel invincible: "It will never happen to me." The "it" might be the possibility of becoming pregnant ("I can't possibly get pregnant"), or of contracting a sexually transmitted disease after having unprotected intercourse ("He/she couldn't possibly have a disease"), or any of the numerous adverse effects of unsafe behavior. This perceived sense of invulnerability was considered to be a stage of cognitive development that adolescents had to pass through on the way to adulthood.

We now have considerable scientific evidence that adolescents do feel vulnerable to contracting a sexually transmitted disease or getting sick

"Now that I am older, I can make choices for myself and think before I act." *Girl, 12*

Understanding teens' new thinking skills

Teens enjoy exercising their budding ability for lively debate. For them, conflicts may just be a way of expressing themselves. Adults, on the other hand, tend to take arguments personally and may view them as intense and disruptive or as a direct threat to their authority.

- Be patient when teens "test drive" their newly acquired reasoning skills, and encourage healthy, respectful debate by setting "rules of engagement."
- Disrespect should never be tolerated by either an adolescent or an adult.
- Never correct or put down adolescents' logic; simply listen to and acknowledge what they say. A good strategy is to ask how they arrived at the thoughts or conclusions they are expressing.
- Don't take it to heart when teens criticize adult opinions and behaviors. They may challenge you, but they still need you.
- Unless a teen has a history of problem behavior, do not worry if he or she demonstrates melodramatic tendencies.
- Remember that not every disagreement is a conflict.

from drinking too much. In fact, several studies have found that adolescents perceive more risk in certain areas than adults do, such as the chance of getting into an accident if they drive with a drunk driver. Teenagers also are not as optimistic as their parents are about avoiding injuries and illness. However, they are less likely than adults to believe poor health will result from experimenting with sex, drinking, drugs, or smoking.

For many adolescents, being aware of the risks involved in a given action fails to stop them from participating. Research is starting to discover that adolescents judge the benefits of partaking in risky behaviors differently than adults do, and this difference in judgment may have a biological basis in the brain. Functional magnetic resonance imaging studies have shown that while winning at gambling, the "reward" center lights up more in teens'

> ## "As an adolescent, I think more for myself now. I am also more aware of the feelings of people around me and more aware of my own feelings."
> *Girl, 15*

brains than in adults' brains, meaning that teens experience greater emotional satisfaction when risk-taking produces a desired outcome.

Teens also may discern social benefits from smoking, drinking, or sexual activity. In schools and communities where the popular students are more likely to smoke, drink, and be sexually experienced, trying out these risky behaviors could be viewed by young people as a rational strategy for gaining approval from their friends and fellow students. Most teens who experiment with alcohol and cigarettes do not develop addictions, but some

do, especially if they start experimentation at an early age.

The upside of perceiving rewards for taking risks is that teens are willing to assume new challenges necessary for adulthood, such as starting a job, leaving home, and forming diverse relationships. In fact, adolescence is the perfect time to strike out in different directions. Only in early childhood are people as receptive to new information as they are in adolescence.

Given the developmental directive to experiment, it is not surprising that scare tactics, school-based abstinence curricula, and "Just say no" cam-

Cognition ignition

Freshly acquired reasoning and logic skills are like a new gadget adolescents are just itching to try out. Here are some ways you can help young people make effective use of their developing capacities:

- Ask open-ended questions that invite thought and debate. This will help adolescents consider their range of options and the natural consequences of each choice.

  - **Example of an open-ended question that invites discussion:**
    "How do you think it will benefit you and/or harm you to quit your after-school job to join the basketball team?"
    (invites thought and debate)

  - **Example of a close-ended question that ellicits a yes or no response:**
    "Will you regret quitting your after-school job to join the basketball team?"

- Never subject an adolescent to public criticism or mockery of their thoughts or ideas.

- Encourage a deeper understanding of issues and topics an adolescent brings up by pointing them to accurate, factual information.

- Make sure teens grasp the role of emotions in the decision-making process—feelings like anger, fear, sadness, or elation can cloud judgment. Decisions, especially important ones, should be made while calm and revisited after "sleeping on it."

- Realize teens bring a variety of strengths—logic, common sense, creative approaches—to the decision-making process.

Adolescents need opportunities to practice and discuss realistic decision-making. Here are some ways adults can facilitate the process:

- Get youth actively practicing decision-making through role-playing and group problem-solving exercises.
- Take a look at how you make decisions and then lead by example.
- Demonstrate to teens how to choose between competing pressures and demands.
- Many adolescents live in the now. Show them the benefits of future thinking by anticipating difficult situations and planning in advance how to handle them.
- Encourage adolescents to spend time with friends who share their values.

paigns have proven to be ineffective with young people. More successful strategies engage youth in using their emerging critical-thinking skills. For example, taking young people through the risks of a certain action or activity and having them assess the situation's consequences at every juncture allows them to develop future-thinking techniques and makes them feel more in control. This tactic challenges their intellect, while simply forbidding them

to do something only challenges their sense of autonomy.

Cognitive mindsets

This section details some of the cognitive mindsets—ways of thinking and believing—experienced by adolescents as a result of brain development.

I don't think that's fair

Advances in reasoning skills lead teens to become interested in fairness

or justice. They are quick to point out inconsistencies between adults' words and their actions. However, the developing adolescent brain makes it difficult for them to see shades of gray or nuances in arguments and opinions. They tend to view things in extremes of black and white, allowing little room for error. Their reasoning skills can be honed by encouraging teens to talk about their views, whether it is their political or spiritual beliefs, or

Sharing your experiences

Adults often support each other by sharing stories about their own experience in a similar situation. This strategy works less well with teens, who may respond to adults' attempts to help this way with exclamations of "You don't understand!" or "My life is ruined!"

Try not to take it personally when young people discount your experiences. Just listen to their concerns and empathize. Seek to understand their feelings first before offering up anecdotes about what you were like as a teen, and when you do, speak about your vulnerabilities and the mistakes that you made at that age. Don't let it all hang out, though. Experts advise that adults talk about their past experiences cautiously and conservatively.

"I am capable of making my own decisions and I challenge myself a lot more since I am not a child anymore." *Boy, 15*

their responses to something they saw on the Internet or in a magazine.

Researcher Laurence Steinberg, PhD, has suggested that adults and adolescents have different views of conflict. It is the parents who get stressed out by dust-ups over daily mundane issues. A possible reason for this is that adults see the decisions in question as stemming from moral distinctions of right and wrong, traditions, social customs, and core beliefs, whereas teens tend to view decisions simply as matters of personal choice.

Take a clean bedroom. Adults view the issue from a moral stand- point (cleanliness is next to godliness; cleaning your room is the right thing to do). An adolescent is more committed to the issue of fairness—my room is my domain; it is not fair for parents to dictate whether my room is neat or messy, and what does it matter in the grand scheme of things? Adolescents are less interested in the moral standpoint, so the conflict may not be as meaningful for them. Therefore, the parent may walk away upset—and stay upset—more often than the young person.

I am taking up the cause

On the one hand, teens are concerned with their appearance and their every move. One consistent experience of adolescence is the constant feeling of being "on stage" and that everyone and everything is centered on their appearance and actions. This preoccupation stems from the fact that brain changes actually spur adolescents to spend an inordinate amount of time thinking about and looking at themselves.

This does not mean young people are inherently selfish. On the contrary, cognitive development also prompts them to become outward-directed and interested in something larger than themselves. Embrace this paradox and accept it.

The newfound ability to consider abstract concepts may make teens want to become involved in things that have deeper meaning. They want to tackle the big issues and are often drawn into causes. This not only widens a young person's perspective but also is greatly empowering. After reading about cruelty to animals, an adolescent may become vegetarian and active in animal rights campaigns. Support their interests and help them find ways large and small they can contribute to the causes in which they believe. This is an excellent way for adolescents to move from self-consciousness to a greater consciousness of the world.

"Being a teenager means thinking about going to college, acting more mature, and being more interested in girls."

Boy, 15

Sleep and Cognitive Development

Teen brains need more Zzzzzzzs

Brain development even affects the way teens sleep. Adolescents' normal sleep patterns are different from those of children and adults. Teens are often drowsy upon waking, tired during the day, and wakeful at night.

Until the age of 10, most children awaken refreshed and energetic. In adolescence, the brain's biological clock, or circadian rhythm, shifts forward. Melatonin secretions, which trigger sleepiness, start later at night and turn off later in the morning. This natural shift peps up adolescents at the traditional weekday bedtime of 9 or 10 p.m. and can explain why it is so hard to rouse them at sunrise. In contrast, circadian rhythms in middle-aged people tend to swing backward, and many parents struggle to stay awake when their adolescent children are at their most alert.

Teenagers actually need as much sleep or more than they got as children—nine to 10 hours are optimum. Most adolescents are chronically sleep-deprived, averaging a scant six to seven hours a night. Part of the blame can be placed on early starting times for school, which, coupled with many teens' 11 p.m. and midnight bedtimes, result in a considerable sleep deficit.

Too little sleep can result in uncontrolled napping (either in class or, more dangerously, behind the wheel), irritability, inability to do tasks that are not exciting or of a competitive nature, and dependence on caffeine drinks to stay alert.

Sleep debt also has a powerful effect on a teen's ability to learn and retain new material, especially in abstract subject areas such as physics, philosophy, math, and calculus.

Battling biology can be daunting, but adults can help teenagers get enough sleep by keeping TVs and electronic gadgets out of their bedrooms, switching to caffeine-free drinks in the evening, and getting them to wind down activity by a reasonable hour. Catch-up sleep on weekends is a second-best option because it can confuse the brain as to when nighttime occurs and is not as restorative as regular slumber.

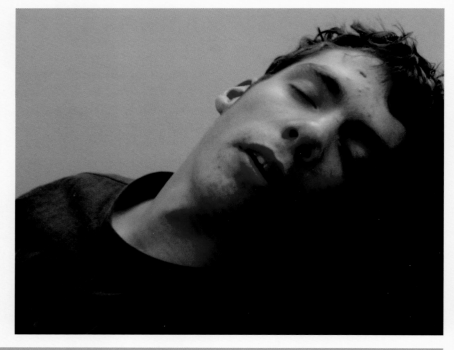

Effects of Tobacco, Alcohol and Drugs on the Developing Adolescent Brain

Risk-taking may be based in biology, but that does not diminish the possible unhealthy consequences of alcohol and other drugs and tobacco on the developing teen brain.

Recent brain research with magnetic resonance imaging suggests that alcohol impacts adolescents differently than it does adults. Young people are more vulnerable to the negative effects of alcohol on the hippocampus—the part of the brain that regulates working memory and learning. Consequently, heavy use of alcohol and other drugs during the teen years can result in lower scores on tests of memory and attention in one's early to mid-20s.

People who begin drinking before age 15 are four times more likely to become alcohol-dependent than those who wait until they are 21. Teens also tend to be less sensitive than adults to alcohol's sedative qualities. Sedation in response to alcohol is one of the ways the body protects itself, since it is impossible to keep drinking once asleep or passed out. Teenagers are able to stay awake longer with higher blood alcohol levels than older drinkers can. This biological difference allows teens to drink more, thereby exposing themselves to greater cognitive impairment and perhaps brain damage from alcohol poisoning.

There are also striking differences in the way nicotine affects adolescent and adult smokers. Nicotine results in cell damage and loss throughout the brain at any age, but in teenagers the damage is worse in the hippocampus, the mind's memory bank. Compared to adults, teen smokers experience more episodes of depression and cardiac irregularities, and are more apt to become quickly and persistently nicotine-dependent.

Drugs such as cocaine and amphetamines target dopamine receptor neurons in the brain, and damage to these neurons may affect adolescent brain development for life in the areas of impulse control and ability to experience reward.

Other effects of substance abuse in adolescents include delays in developing executive functions (judgment, planning and completing tasks, meeting goals) and overblown and immature emotional responses to situations.

CHAPTER 3

EMOTIONAL & SOCIAL DEVELOPMENT

A quest for emotional and social competence

> "Adults influence me more than my friends because they have more wisdom and experience in the world."
>
> *Girl, 16*

Although the stereotype of adolescence emphasizes emotional outbursts and mood swings, in truth, the teen years are a quest for emotional and social competence.

Emotional competence is the ability to perceive, assess, and manage one's own emotions. Social competence is the capacity to be sensitive and effective in relating to other people. Cognitive development in the adolescent brain gives teens increasing capacity to manage their emotions and relate well to others.

Unlike the physical changes of puberty, emotional and social development is not an inevitable biological process during adolescence. Society expects that young people will learn to prevent their emotions from interfering with performance and relate well to other people, but this does not occur from brain development alone—it must be cultivated.

Four areas of emotional and social development

Emotional and social development work in concert: through relating to others, you gain insights into yourself. The skills necessary for managing emotions and successful relationships have been called "emotional intelligence" and include self-awareness, social awareness, self-management, and the ability to get along with others and make friends.

Self-awareness: What do I feel?

Self-awareness centers on young people learning to recognize and name their emotions. Feelings cannot be labeled accurately unless conscious attention is paid to them, and that involves going deeper than saying one feels "good," "bad," or the all-purpose "OK."

Going deeper means an adolescent might discover he or she feels "anxious" about an upcoming test, or "sad" when rejected by a potential love interest. Identifying the source of a feeling can lead to figuring out constructive ways to resolve a problem.

Without this awareness, undefined feelings can become uncomfortable enough that adolescents may grow withdrawn or depressed or pursue such numbing behaviors as drinking alcohol, using drugs, or overeating.

Social awareness: What do other people feel?

While it is vital that youth recognize their own emotions, they must also develop empathy and take into account

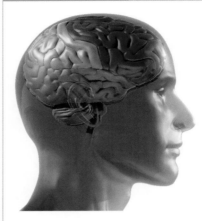

BRAIN BOX

Increases in estrogen and testosterone at puberty literally change the brain structure so that it processes social situations differently. Pubertal hormones prompt a proliferation of receptors for oxytocin, a hormone that functions as a neurotransmitter, in the limbic area of the brain, where emotional processing occurs. The effect of increased oxytocin is to increase feelings of self-consciousness, to the point where an adolescent may truly feel that his or her behavior is the focus of everyone else's attention. These feelings of having the world as an audience peak around age 15 and then decline.

SOURCE: Steinberg, L. (2008) A social neuroscience perspective on adolescent risk-taking. *Developmental Review*, 28, 78–106.

the feelings of others. Understanding the thoughts and feelings of others and appreciating the value of human differences are the cornerstones of social awareness.

Cognitive development during adolescence may make social awareness difficult for some young people. Adolescents actually read emotions through a different part of the brain than do adults. Dr. Deborah Yurgelun-Todd, director of Neuropsychology and Cognitive Neuroimaging at McLean Hospital in Belmont, Massachusetts, took magnetic resonance imaging (MRI) scans of the brains of both teenagers and adults as they were shown images of faces that clearly expressed fear. All the adults correctly identified fear. About half of the teens got it wrong, mistaking the expression as that of shock, sadness, or confusion.

Yurgelun-Todd discovered that on the MRI scans of the adults, both the limbic area of the brain (the part of the brain linked to emotions) and the prefrontal cortex (connected to judgment and reasoning) were lit up. When teens saw the same images, the limbic area was bright, but there was almost no activity in the prefrontal cortex. Until the prefrontal cortex fully develops in

early adulthood, teens may misinterpret body language and facial expressions. Adults can help by telling teens how they are feeling. For example, a parent can say, "I'm not mad at you, just tired and crabby."

Self-management: How can I control my emotions?

Self-management is monitoring and regulating one's emotions and establishing and working toward positive goals. Adolescents can experience intense emotions with puberty. Researchers have found that the increase of testosterone in both boys and girls at puberty literally swells the amygdala, an area of the brain associated with social acceptance, responses to reward, and emotions, especially fear.

Nonetheless, adolescents can and do learn to manage their emotions. Self-management in a young person involves using developing reasoning and abstract thinking skills to step back, examine emotions, and consider how those emotions bear on longer-term goals. By actively managing emotions rather than reacting to a flood of feelings, young people can learn to avoid the pitfalls and problems that strong emotions often evoke. Recognizing that they have the power to choose how to react in a situation can greatly improve the way adolescents experience that situation.

Peer relationships: How can I make and keep friends?

Social and emotional development depends on establishing and maintaining healthy, rewarding relationships based on cooperation, effective communication, and the ability to resolve conflict and resist inappropriate peer pressure.

These social skills are fostered by involvement in a peer group, and teens generally prefer to spend increasing amounts of time with fellow adolescents and less time with family. Peers provide a new opportunity for young people to form necessary social skills and an identity outside the family.

Possible causes of heightened emotions in adolescents

- Hormones, which set off physical changes at puberty, also affect moods and general emotional responses in teens.
- Concerns about physical changes—height, weight, facial hair, developing breasts in girls—are a source of sensitivity and heightened emotions.
- Irregular meal patterns, skipping breakfast, and fasting to lose weight can affect mood.
- Inadequate sleep can lead to moodiness, gloominess, irritability, and a tendency to overreact.
- Experiencing the normal ups and downs of social relationships, especially romantic relationships, can make a teen feel anything from elation to abject despair.

The influence of peers is normal and expected. Peers have significant sway on day-to-day values, attitudes, and behaviors in relation to school, as well as tastes in clothing and music. Peers also play a central role in the development of sexual identities and the formation of intimate friendships and romantic relationships.

Friends need not be a threat to parents' ultimate authority. Parents remain central throughout adolescence. Young people depend on their families and adult caregivers for affection, identification, values, and decision-making skills. Teens report, and research confirms, that parents have more influence than peers on whether or not adolescents smoke, use alcohol and other drugs, or initiate sexual intercourse.

Teens also frequently seek out adult role models and advisors such

"My mom is my biggest influence because she always knows the answers to my questions and would never tell me anything that would hurt me in the long run." *Boy, 15*

Popularity plusses and minuses

Most parents wish their teenagers to be popular. Certainly, most teens want to be popular, too. However, a recent study in the journal *Child Development* suggests that being on the A-list is not always what it's cracked up to be.

The advantages of popularity are that popular adolescents possess a broader array of social skills than their less well-liked peers, better self-concepts, a greater ability to form meaningful relationships with both friends and parents, and greater ability to resolve conflicts within these relationships.

But there is a downside. Popular teens are at higher risk for exposure to—and participation in—whatever risky behaviors are condoned by their peers. Popularity can be associated with higher levels of alcohol and substance abuse and minor deviant behavior, such as vandalism and shoplifting.

Popular kids tend to get along better with their friends and family members and seem to have more emotional maturity than others. This maturity can be compromised by their need for group approval, as popular teens may be even more willing than other teens to adopt behaviors they think will earn them greater acceptance. Sometimes the behaviors are "pro-social"—as when a group pressures popular members to be less aggressive and hostile. Sometimes, when risky behaviors are valued by popular kids, the behaviors are more deviant.

SOURCE: Allen, J.P., Porter, M.R., & McFarland, F.C. (2005). The two faces of adolescents' success with peers: adolescent popularity, social adaptation, and deviant behavior. *Child Development*. 76(3), 747–760.

as teachers, relatives, club leaders, or neighbors. Studies show that connections to teachers, for example, can be just as protective as connections to parents in delaying the initiation of sexual activity and use of drugs, alcohol, and tobacco.

Some teenagers, of course, trade the influence of parents and other adults for the influence of their peers,

but this usually happens when family closeness and parental monitoring are missing. Youth need to learn independent-thinking, decision-making, and problem-solving skills from their parents or guardians and other caring adults, so they can apply these skills within their peer network.

The nature of social relationships changes as adolescents get older. Younger teens typically have at least one primary group of friends, and the members are usually similar in many respects, including gender. During the early teen years, both boys and girls are concerned with conforming and being accepted by their peer group.

"A good parent listens to you and does not look down on you."

Girl, 14

Emerging brain science indicates that during early adolescence social acceptance by peers may be processed by the brain similarly to other pleasurable rewards, such as receiving money or eating ice cream. This makes social acceptance highly desirable and helps explain why adolescents change their behavior to match their peers'. Teens often adopt the styles, values, and interests of the group to maintain an identity that distinguishes their group from other students.

Peer groups in middle adolescence (14-16 years) tend to contain both boys and girls, and group members are more tolerant of differences in appearance, beliefs, and feelings. By late adolescence (17-19 years), young people have diversified their peer network beyond a single clique or crowd and develop intimate relationships within these peer groups, such as one-on-one friendships and romances.

Dating is a way to develop social skills, learn about other people, and explore romantic and sexual feelings. The hormonal changes that accompany puberty move adolescents toward dating relationships. Mainstream culture plays a role as well. Media and popular culture are awash in images and messages that promote adolescent sexuality and romance. Dating can lead to sexual activity, but also to opportunities for expanded emotional growth. Dating and friendships open up an adolescent to experiencing extremes of happiness, excitement, disappointment, and despair. Recent research has shown that both boys and girls value intimacy in romantic relationships, dispelling the prevailing stereotype that boys prefer casual sexual relationships.

Emotional and social development in context

Adolescents face an astonishing array of options in modern society—everything from choosing multiple sources of entertainment to deciding among alternative educational or vocational pathways. Teenagers are confronted with more decisions, and more complicated decisions, than their parents and grandparents faced, often in complex environments that trigger conflicting feelings and desires.

Responsible decision-making involves generating, implementing, and evaluating ethical choices in a given situation. The choices ideally will benefit both the decision-maker and the well-being of others.

The still-developing frontal lobes in the brain render adolescents vulnerable to making poor decisions; they can have trouble forming judgments when things are cloudy or uncertain. The Cognitive Development chapter gives strategies for helping young people with their decision-making skills.

Decisions about risk-taking often are made in group situations—settings that activate intense feelings and trigger impulses. In a recent experimental study, teenagers, college students, and adults were asked to play a video driving game. When participants were alone, levels of risky driving were the same for the teens, college students, and adults. However, when they played the game in front of friends, risky driving doubled among the adolescents and increased by 50 percent among the college students, but remained unchanged among the adults. Risky behavior increased for both boys and girls.

In a follow-up study, Laurence Steinberg, PhD, of Temple University used functional MRI to map brain activity during the video driving game. The brain scans showed that teen brains respond differently when peers are present compared to when they are not present. When teens played the driving game alone, brain regions linked to cognitive control and reasoning were activated. When peers were present, additional brain circuitry that processes rewards was also activated,

The building blocks of empathy

Empathy is the ability to identify with another person's concerns and feelings. Empathy is the foundation of tolerance, compassion, and the ability to differentiate right from wrong. Empathy motivates teens and adults alike to care for those who are hurt or troubled.

Ways you can help build empathy in an adolescent:

- Demonstrate tolerance and generosity in your thoughts, words, and actions.

- Actively participate in religious or social organizations that ask you to focus on issues larger than yourself.

- Fine-tune your own empathetic behaviors and act on your concerns to comfort others, so that teenagers can copy your actions.

- Build a young person's emotional vocabulary by using such "feelings" statements as "Your friend seems really (anxious, mad, discouraged)." You can also point out nonverbal feeling cues to a teenager.

- Teach empathy and awareness of others, such as helping youth understand on an emotional level the negative consequences of prejudice.

- Talk with a young person about how his or her own suffering can lead to compassion for other teens who experience suffering.

suggesting that, for teens, potentially rewarding—and potentially risky—behaviors become even more gratifying in the presence of peers. By late adolescence and early adulthood, the cognitive control network matures, so that even among friends in a high-pressure situation, the urge to take risks diminishes.

Because heightened vulnerability to peer influence and risk-taking ap-

pears to be a natural and normal part of neurobiological development, telling adolescents not to give in to peer influence may not be effective, especially during early adolescence. Instead, teens may be best protected from harm through limiting exposure to risky situations. Harm-reducing tactics include raising the price of cigarettes, rigorously policing the sale of alcohol to minors, placing restrictions on

teen driving, and making reproductive health services more accessible to adolescents.

"A good friend is 100% real with you all the time."

Boy, 16

WAYS TO HELP TEENS MAKE HEALTHY SOCIAL CONNECTIONS

Discuss the meaning of true friendship

People have plenty of acquaintances, but true friends can be rare gifts. Talk with young people about what distinguishes true friends from situational friends. True friends like you for yourself. They try to help and encourage you, and they stand by you when the other kids make fun of you or give you a hard time. A true friend does not judge you by the clothes you wear or how much expensive stuff you have, pressure you to go along with the crowd, make you do dangerous or illegal things, or leave you high and dry when things get rough.

Help teens get involved in things they care about

Young people can make friends at school, but they can also form relationships through mutual interests. Find out what adolescents are interested in—computers, music, dance, poetry slams, sports, science fiction/fantasy—and help start a club, or get teens involved in existing organizations.

Find role models for friendship

Examples of good friendships abound in movies, books, and songs, and also in your community. Friendship could be the theme of a book club or a movie series in a youth program. Expose adolescents to real-life role models and then discuss what good friendships have in common. What attributes or values do these people share?

Promote service to others

Getting youth involved with a service project in your community is a way to strengthen friendships, both with people their own age and across the generations, and to make social connections through the pursuit of common goals. Community service also promotes the values of caring and kindness, and it helps adolescents develop a sense of empathy. Let teens decide what kind of service project they would like to do.

Teach about the relationship between honesty and tact

Friends don't tear each other down—even in the name of honesty. You can help sharpen a young person's decision-making skills by talking about ways of handling certain situations without being hurtful. Possible scenarios include what to say when someone asks, "Do you like my new haircut?" or what to say when a friend or relative mentions, "I've never seen you wear the sweater I gave you."

Talk about boundaries

Being a friend does not mean being a doormat or being joined at the hip 24/7. Friendships need boundaries, just as other relationships do. Stress the importance of boundaries, establishing limits, and respecting privacy and "alone time," which make friendships healthier and stronger in the long run.

Teen Stress

Teens feel the pressure

"I think stress is a problem for teenagers like me…because when you get a certain age, you start worrying about certain things, like, when your puberty comes, your body starts to develop more, and then you get to worry about school, your families, and what most people think about you."   Girl, 14

You may have caught yourself thinking, "Teen stress? Wait until they're older—then they'll know stress."

Yet teen stress is an important health issue. The early teen years are marked by rapid changes—physical, cognitive, and emotional. Young people also face changing relationships with peers, new demands at school, family tensions, and safety issues in their communities. The ways in which teens cope with these stressors can have significant short- and long-term consequences on their physical and emotional health. Difficulties in handling stress can lead to mental health problems, such as depression and anxiety disorders.

What is stress? It is the body's reaction to a challenge, which could be anything from outright physical danger to asking someone for a date or trying out for a sports team. Good and bad things create stress. Getting into a fight with a friend is stressful, but so is a passionate kiss and contemplating what might follow.

The human body responds to stressors by activating the nervous system and specific hormones. The hypothalamus signals the adrenal glands to produce more of the hormones adrenaline and cortisol and release them into the bloodstream. The hormones speed

THINGS THAT CAN CAUSE YOUTH STRESS

- School pressure and career decisions
- After-school or summer jobs
- Dating and friendships
- Pressure to wear certain types of clothing, jewelry, or hairstyles
- Pressure to experiment with drugs, alcohol, or sex
- Pressure to be a particular size or body shape. With girls, the focus is often weight. With boys, it is usually a certain muscular or athletic physique.
- Dealing with the physical and cognitive changes of puberty
- Family and peer conflicts
- Being bullied or exposed to violence or sexual harassment
- Crammed schedules, juggling school, sports, after-school activities, social life, and family obligations

up heart rate, breathing rate, blood pressure, and metabolism. Blood vessels open wider to let more blood flow to large muscle groups, pupils dilate to improve vision, and the liver

releases stored glucose to increase the body's energy. This physical response to stress kicks in much more quickly in teens than in adults because the part of the brain that can calmly assess danger and call off the stress response, the prefrontal cortex, is not fully developed in adolescence.

The stress response prepares a person to react quickly and perform well under pressure. It can help teens be on their toes and ready to rise to a challenge.

The stress response can cause problems, however, when it overreacts or goes on for too long. Long-term stressful situations, like coping with a parent's divorce or being bullied at school, can produce a lasting, low-level stress that can wear out the body's reserves, weaken the immune system, and make an adolescent feel depleted or beleaguered.

The things that cause adolescents stress are often different from what stresses adults. Adolescents will have different experiences from one another, as well. A good example of this can be seen by observing teens at a dance.

Some are hunched in the corner, eyes downcast and hugging the wall. They can't wait for the night to be over. Others are out there dancing their feet off, talking and laughing and hoping the music never stops. In between, you may find a few kids pretending to be bored, hanging out with their friends, and maybe venturing onto the floor for a dance or two. So, is the dance uniformly stressful?

Several strategies can help teens with their stress. It is best, whenever possible, to help teens address stressful situations immediately. Listen to them, be open, and realize that you can be supportive even if you cannot relate to what they are feeling. Tune in to your own levels of stress, since your over-whelmed feelings can be contagious. For chronic stress, parents or caring adults can help teens understand the cause of the stress and then identify and practice positive ways to manage the situation.

SIGNS AN ADOLESCENT IS OVERLOADED

- Increased complaints of headache, stomachache, muscle pain, tiredness
- Shutting down and withdrawing from people and activities
- Increased anger or irritability; i.e., lashing out at people and situations
- Crying more often and appearing teary-eyed
- Feelings of hopelessness
- Chronic anxiety and nervousness
- Changes in sleeping and eating habits, i.e., insomnia or being "too busy" to eat
- Difficulty concentrating

STRESS MANAGEMENT SKILLS FOR YOUNG PEOPLE—& ADULTS

- Talk about problems with others
- Take deep breaths, accompanied by thinking or saying aloud, "I can handle this"
- Perform progressive muscle relaxation, which involves repeatedly tensing and relaxing large muscles of the body
- Set small goals and break tasks into smaller, manageable chunks
- Exercise and eat regular meals
- Get proper sleep
- Break the habit of relying on caffeine or energy drinks to get through the day
- Focus on what you can control (your reactions, your actions) and let go of what you cannot (other people's opinions and expectations)
- Visualize and practice feared situations
- Work through worst-case scenarios until they seem amusing or absurd
- Lower unrealistic expectations
- Schedule breaks and enjoyable activities
- Accept yourself as you are; identify your unique strengths and build on them
- Give up on the idea of perfection, both in yourself and in others

SOURCE: Dyl, J. Helping teens cope with stress. *Lifespan.* Retrieved from www.lifespan.org/services/childhealth/parenting/teen-stress.htm

Bullying

Teen bullying: A part of growing up?

Most adults can remember being teased or bullied when they were younger. It may be regarded as a regular—albeit nasty—part of growing up, but research has shown that bullying has far-reaching negative effects on adolescents. This all-too-common experience can lead to serious problems for young people at a critical time in their development, including poor mental health and dropping out of school.

Estimates from a 2002 CDC survey reveal that approximately 30 percent of teens in the United States, or over 5.7 million teens, have been involved in bullying as a victim, spectator, or perpetrator. In a 2001 national survey of students in grades six to 10, 13 percent reported bullying others, 11 percent reported being the target of school bullies, and another 6 percent said they bullied others and were bullied themselves. Teen bullying appears to be much more common among younger teens than older teens. As teens grow older, they are less likely to bully others and to be the targets of bullies.

Bullying involves a person or a group repeatedly trying to harm someone they see as weaker or more vulnerable. Appearance and social status are the main reasons for bullying, but young people can be singled out because of their sexual orientation, their race or religion, or because they may be shy and introverted.

Bullying can involve direct attacks—hitting, threatening or intimidating, maliciously teasing and taunting, name-calling, making sexual remarks, sexual assault, and stealing or damaging belongings. Bullying can also involve the subtler, indirect attacks of rumor-mongering or encouraging others to snub someone. New technology, such as text messaging, instant messaging, social networking websites, and the easy filming and online posting of videos, has introduced a new form of intimidation—cyberbullying—which is widespread on the Internet.

Debunking the myth of the bully

The typical portrait of a young bully is someone who is insecure and seething with self-loathing. The latest research indicates the opposite is often true, that teen bullies—both boys and girls—tend to be confident, with high self-esteem and elevated social status among their peers.

Despite bullies' social status, their classmates would rather not spend a lot of time with them. Nonetheless, bullies' stature means that other teens tolerate bullying behavior. This can

WARNING SIGNS

- Damaged or missing clothing and belongings
- Unexplained cuts, bruises, or torn clothes
- Lack of friends
- Frequent claims of having lost pocket money, possessions, packed lunches, or snacks
- Fear of school or of leaving the house
- Avoidance of places, friends, family members, or activities teens once enjoyed
- Unusual routes to and from school or the bus stop
- Poor appetite, headaches, stomachaches
- Mood swings
- Trouble sleeping
- Lack of interest in schoolwork
- Talk about suicide
- Uncharacteristic aggression toward younger siblings or family members

SOURCE: The Youth Connection, January/February 2005, Institute for Youth Development, www.youthdevelopment.org

TAKING THE BARK OUT OF BULLIES

Bullying should not be shrugged off as a normal rite of passage in adolescence. It is abusive behavior that is likely to create emotional and social problems during the teen years and later in life for both the victim and the aggressor. Here is how adults can help:

- **SPEAK UP** after a teen tells you about being bullied at school or elsewhere. Take his or her concerns seriously. Go to the school and talk to the teachers, coaches, and principal. Speak to the parents or adults in charge if a teen is being harassed by a peer or social clique.

- **OBSERVE** your own behavior. Adolescents look to adults for cues as to how to act, so practice being caring and empathetic, and controlling your aggressions. Avoid engaging in physical violence, harsh criticism, vendettas, and vicious emotional outbursts.

- **ADVOCATE** for policies and programs concerning bullying in the schools and the community. Anti-bullying policies have been adopted by state boards of education in North Carolina, Oregon, California, New York, Florida, and Louisiana.

One successful program used throughout the country has been developed by Dan Olweus, a Norwegian psychologist and bullying expert. The program focuses on creating a "caring community" as opposed to eliminating bad behavior. For more information on the Olweus Bullying Prevention Program, go to http://www.clemson.edu/olweus/.

pose challenges for those addressing bullying problems.

Bullies also tend to be physically aggressive, impulsive, and quick to anger, which fits in with the profile of a classic intimidator. Most often, adolescent bullies are mirroring behavior they have seen in their home or observed in adults.

School bullying

School bullying occurs more frequently among boys than among girls. Teenage boys are more likely both to bully others and to be the targets of bullies. While both boys and girls say others bully them by making fun of the way they look or talk, boys are more likely to report being hit, shoved, or punched. Girls are more often the targets of rumors and sexual comments, but fighting does occur.

While teenage boys target both boys and girls, teenage girls most often bully other girls, using sly and more indirect forms of aggression than boys, such as spreading gossip or urging others to reject or exclude another girl.

Harassment hurts

Bullying can make teens feel stressed, anxious, and afraid. Adolescent victims of bullying may not be able to concentrate in school, a problem that can lead to avoiding classes, sports, and social situations. If the bullying continues for long periods of time, feelings of self-worth suffer. Bullied teens can become isolated and withdrawn. In rare cases, adolescents may take drastic measures, such as carrying weapons for protection.

One of the most common psychiatric disorders found in adolescents who are bullied is depression, an illness which, if left untreated, can interfere with their ability to function. According to a 2007 study linking bullying and suicidal behavior, adolescents who were frequently bullied in school were five times as likely to have serious suicidal thoughts and four times as likely to attempt suicide as students who had not been victims.

Even after the bullying has stopped, its effects can linger. Researchers have found that years later,

adults who were bullied as teens have higher levels of depression and poorer self-esteem than other adults.

Bullies also fare less well in adulthood. Being a teen bully can be a warning sign of future troubles. Teens, particularly boys, who bully are more likely to engage in other delinquent behaviors in early adulthood, such as vandalism, shoplifting, truancy, and drug use. They are four times more likely than non-bullies to be convicted of crimes by age 24, with 60 percent of bullies having at least one criminal conviction.

CYBERBULLIES

Text messaging, social networking sites, blogs, email, instant messaging—all these are ways teens stay connected to each other and express who they are to the world.

However, this new technology can make young people vulnerable to the age-old problem of bullying. Unmonitored social networking sites and chat rooms can be a forum for messages that are sexually provocative, demeaning, violence-based, or racist.

Cyberbullies send harassing or obscene messages, post private information on a public site, intentionally exclude someone from a chat room, or pretend to be someone else to try to embarrass a person (for example, by pretending to be a boy or girl who is romantically interested in the person).

Cyberbullying can spiral into a "flame war"—an escalation of online attacks sent back and forth, either privately through text and instant messaging or on a public site. On public sites flaming is meant to humiliate the person attacked and drive him or her away from the web site or forum.

Often, the information used for cyberbullying at first appears innocent or inconsequential. A teen could post or text what he or she thinks is run-of-the-mill news about a friend, teacher, or family member, but others could use it for harassment or bullying purposes.

Although there is still very little research on cyberbullying, it appears

to occur at about the same rate as traditional bullying. A 2007 study of middle schools in the Southeast found

that boys and girls are equally likely to engage in cyberbullying, but girls are more likely to be victims. Twenty-five percent of girls and 17 percent of boys reported having been victims of cyberbullying in the past couple of months. Over one-third of victims of electronic bullying in this study also reported bullying behaviors. Instant messaging is the most common method for cyberbullying.

Cyberbullying differs from traditional bullying in that it can be harder to escape. It can occur at any time of the day or night, and it can be much more public, since rude and obscene messages

can be spread quickly. It also can be anonymous. In the same 2007 study of middle school students, almost half of the victims of cyberbullying did not know who had bullied them.

Cyberbullying is much more common than online sexual solicitation, another serious concern. Most online sex crimes involve adult men soliciting teens between the ages of 12 and 17 into meeting them to have sex. The common media portrayal of teen victims as naïve is largely false. The vast majority of teens who are victims of online sexual predators know they are communicating with adults, communicate online about sex, and expect to have a romantic or sexual experience if and when they meet. About three-quarters of teens who meet the offender meet them more than once. To help teens avoid becoming victims of online sex crimes, it is important to have accurate and candid discussions about how it is wrong for adults to take advantage of normal sexual feelings among teens.

Teens are more vulnerable to sexual solicitations online if they send (not just post) private information to someone unknown, visit chat rooms, access pornography, or make sexual remarks online themselves.

There is no evidence that use of social networking sites such as Facebook or MySpace increases a teen's risk of aggressive sexual solicitation.

SOURCES: Gengler, C. (2009). Teens and the internet. *Teen Talk: A Survival Guide for Parents of Teenagers.* Regents of the University of Minnesota. Available at http://www.extension.umn.edu/distribution/familydevelopment/00145.pdf.
Gengler, C. (2009). Teens and social networking websites. *Teen Talk: A Survival Guide for Parents of Teenagers.* Available at http://www.extension.umn.edu/distribution/familydevelopment/00144.pdf.

WAYS ADULTS CAN
PROTECT TEENS
FROM CYBERBULLIES AND PREDATORS

- Stress to teens what is not safe to put on the web or give out to people they don't know: their full name, address, cell phone number, specific places they hang out, financial information, ethnic background, school, or anything else that would help someone locate them. Although it is important to protect young people's privacy, it may be necessary to review a teen's social networking site to make sure they do not reveal too much personal information.

- Emphasize that in cyberspace, there's no such thing as an "erase" button—messages, photos, rants, and musings can and do hang around forever. Information that may seem harmless now to a teen can be used against them at any time—maybe in the future when applying to college or looking for a job. Photos posted on the sites should not reveal too much personal information about teens.

- Shut down a personal website or blog when the adolescent is subjected to bullying or flaming. If necessary, it is possible get a new email address and instant-messaging (IM) identity.

- Make clear to young people what kinds of messages are harmful and inappropriate. Enforce clearly spelled-out consequences if young people engage in those behaviors.

- Encourage teens not to respond to cyberbullying. The decision whether to erase messages is difficult. It is not good for teens to revisit them, but they may need to be saved as evidence if the bullying becomes persistent.

- Keep computers out of teens' bedrooms so that computer activity can be monitored better.

SOURCES: Kowalski, R.M. & Limber, S.P. (2007). Electronic bullying among middle school students. *Journal of Adolescent Health*, 41, S22–S30.
Wolak, J., Finkelhor, D., Mitchell, K.J., & Ybarra, M.L. (2008). Online "predators" and their victims: myths, realities, and implications for prevention and treatment. *American Psychologist*, 63(2): 111–128.

FORMING AN IDENTITY

Building a sense of self

"Part of your identity is knowing who you are, what you want, and when to do the right thing." *Girl, 15*

Adolescence is the first time in life when a person intensely contemplates the question, "Who am I?" The answer to that question—which will continue to evolve over a person's lifetime—forms the basis of personal identity, or one's sense of self. Changes in the adolescent brain give teenagers the tools to start building a personal identity.

Identify is one's sense of self. Two key aspects of identity are self-concept and self-esteem.

Self-concept—or what a person believes about him or herself—is determined by a person's perceptions about his or her talents, qualities, goals, and life experiences. Self-concept can also include religious or political beliefs. For example, a teen's self-concept may be based on her belief that she is smart, artistic, politically conservative, and interested in becoming a doctor. A teen's self-concept is also likely to be influenced by identification with an ethnic group and the experiences he or she has as a result of that connection.

Self-esteem, on the other hand, refers to how people feel about their self-concept—that is, do they have high regard for who they are? Self-esteem is affected by approval from parents and other adults, the level of support received from friends and family, and personal success. Ups and downs in self-esteem are normal during adolescence, particularly in the early teenage years (around middle school). Self-esteem becomes more stable as teens grow older.

During the second decade of life young people are figuring out their self-concept and self-esteem, in part, through five developmental tasks:

- becoming independent
- achieving mastery or a sense of competence
- establishing social status
- experiencing intimacy
- determining sexual identity

By trying on different ways of being, adolescents see what fits in each of these areas. They experiment with what it feels like to hold different ideas, dress different ways, hang out with different kinds of friends, and try new things.

Adolescents will approach this exploration in their own way, and at their own pace. This is a healthy aspect of growing up and should be no cause for alarm.

Because their frontal lobes, which control reasoning, planning, emotions, and problem-solving, are not fully developed, experimentation is

BRAIN BOX

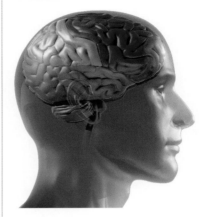

Recent studies have indicated that as adolescents' abstract reasoning skills increase, so do their levels of social anxiety. Abstract reasoning means being able to see yourself from the perspective of an observer, and also to think about other people's thoughts and feelings. The emergence of abstract reasoning may make adolescents more vulnerable to social anxiety because they simultaneously become more self-aware and worry more about what other people are thinking about them.

SOURCE: Rosso, IM, Young, A.D., Femia, L.A., & Yurgelun-Todd, D.A. (2004). Cognitive and emotional components of frontal lobe functioning in adulthood and adolescence. *Annals of the New York Academy of Sciences*, 1021, 355-362.

not always balanced by the capacity to make sound judgments or to see into the not-so-distant future. Consequently, adolescents may take part in risky and daring behaviors while trying on new identities and ways of thinking. Cognitive changes in the brain often promote the adrenaline rush of thrill-seeking and testing of boundaries.

Becoming independent: I can do things on my own and think for myself!

From birth, children start developing autonomy, or the ability to think and act independently. During the teen years, achieving autonomy means becoming a self-governing person.

As they develop autonomy, or independence, adolescents exercise their increasing ability to make and follow through on their own decisions and to formulate their own principles of right and wrong. Healthy identity is derived in part from young people's learning to trust their capacity to make appropriate choices for themselves.

There are two kinds of autonomy—physical and psychological. *Physical autonomy* is the capacity to do things on one's own, beyond the family. As teens gain physical autonomy, they take more responsibility for themselves. Tasks like making sure they have everything ready for school the next day are done independently from parents.

Psychological autonomy is the capacity to independently exercise judgment and to work out one's own principles of right and wrong. As teens gain psychological autonomy they begin to assert their own opinions and point out when the adults in their lives make mistakes.

Developing autonomy often means trying out different ways of behaving, thinking, and believing. While it may not be easy for adults to deal with the "Who am I this time?" aspects of adolescence, achieving autonomy is necessary if a teen is to become self-sufficient in later years. As teens develop autonomy, they have more

How self-esteem impacts teens

While fostering high self-esteem is certainly important in a child's healthy development, feeling good about oneself does not necessarily protect against risky behavior, as was once thought. For example, high self-esteem does not prevent adolescent childbearing, gang involvement, or violence.

contact with the outside world and, at the same time, may require more privacy and time alone.

It is important to remember that young people are taking steps toward independence, but they are not skilled at autonomy. The parts of the brain which control reasoning, planning, and problem-solving are not fully developed in adolescents. Thus teens are unable to accurately assess risk in a situation. They both need and want limit-setting to function and grow.

To be of the most benefit to adolescents, an adult needs to be a consistent figure who provides and maintains safe boundaries in which the young person can practice their independence

skills. Safe boundaries include clearly set and enforced expectations for responsible behavior. Expectations tend to be successfully enforced when they are explicit, practical, age-appropriate, and agreed upon by both the adults and adolescents involved. Both sides should be flexible, and adults especially may want to stress what *to* do in a given situation, rather than focusing on what *not* to do or employing scare tactics.

Setting limits does not mean telling an adolescent how to think or feel. Telling an adolescent—or a person of any age, for that matter—how that person should feel about something, or shaming a person by saying their thinking on a subject is wrong or "bad," prevents his or her healthy development. Adolescents who report that their parents do not grant them the autonomy to think their own thoughts and to feel their own emotions are more likely to be depressed and to act out by getting drunk, skipping school, or fighting.

Achieving a sense of mastery: Am I competent? What do I enjoy doing, and what am I good at?

It is essential to realize teens are trying to gain a sense of competence, which centers on being good at something or achieving goals. Competence is the capacity to master something that others value. Adolescents strive to prove they are competent in school, sports, and work settings, as well as in the social realm, with relationships with peers and family members.

A wide-ranging body of research indicates that adolescents who score high on measures of perceived competence are less susceptible to negative feelings and depression. Adolescents who have a sense of competence generally cope better when they are under stress.

Adolescents need to assess what their competency and personal goals are—what they currently do well, and

How to support healthy identity formation

- Accept the adolescent for who she or he is.
- Respect the differences between the two of you.
- Negotiate with teenagers, especially when establishing limits, and explain your reasoning.
- Practice consistency in enforcing rules.
- Encourage a young person's self-expression.
- Take the teen's point of view into account when reasoning with him or her.

SOURCE: Steinberg, L. and Levine, A. (1997). *You and your adolescent,* New York: Harper Perennial, (pp. 191–193).

Peer pressure and gangs

A major concern with respect to the influence of peer pressure is gang involvement.

Young people are involved in gangs in many different ways. Some teenagers may be hangers-on and not immersed in gang goings-on, while others may have friends in the gang and occasionally get involved. The next levels are regulars who hang out with members most of the time and hard-core members with an all-encompassing involvement in gang activities and recruiting new people.

Gangs differ from groups and cliques in that they can provide a feeling of identity and belonging far beyond just fitting in. Gangs offer a sense of family, respect, and personal security. This familial bond is often stronger than those between teenagers and their natural families since gang members are willing to die and kill for each other and to protect their turf. The utter loyalty to one another is often an airtight bond hard to break and even harder to resist for adolescents who lack this support and constancy in their home lives.

Teenagers join gangs because they want the feelings of safety, companionship, economic opportunity, and excitement. There is often intense pressure to join a gang, and often that pressure can come from older brothers and sisters. However, the feeling of safety in a gang is frequently an illusion, and any economic opportunity is very short-term. The risky or illegal behavior exploits teenagers and will not allow them long-term success or happiness.

Being in a gang is associated with delinquency and disconnection from school and family, as well as an increased risk of death, injury, drug and alcohol abuse, sexually transmitted infections, and teenage parenthood.

"What I like most about my best friend is that she is comfortable in her own skin." *Girl, 12*

in which areas they are willing to strive for success. Those with teenage children or who work with adolescents can encourage them to test their interests. Parents can help them to find at least one skill that they are good at and can master, or encourage involvement in multiple groups or activities within school, religious settings, and the community.

Adolescents may frequently change their minds about what they want to do, which can be frustrating, but adults can still react positively by suggesting they stick with something long enough to establish some skills before moving on to the next pursuit or activity.

This is a time when adults can move beyond the standard role of authority figures. Instead of solving adolescents' problems or telling them what to do, adults can guide teens through the often emotional decision-

making process of figuring out where and when to shine.

Establishing status: Where do I fit in?

One of the many fascinating contradictions in adolescence is that teens desire independence, and at the same time have a deep need to fit in and belong. On one hand, young people may cry, "Leave me alone," but on the other hand they gravitate toward particular groups with which they feel an affinity—the geeks, the jocks, the brains, the hip-hoppers, the Goths, or the A-list. This seemingly contradictory behavior is a predictable part of the identity-formation process.

The impulse to join a group is thought to stem in part from changes in the teen brain. Social acceptance by peers triggers stronger positive emotions (a bigger "reward response") during the teen years than it does in

adulthood. Being part of a group offers teens opportunities to learn and practice the new roles they will take on as adult members of society.

In addition, most teens find it supportive to be part of a group going through the same transitions. Teens often feel unsure about what grown-up life will be like and wonder whether they will succeed or fail when it is their time to contribute. This ambiguity is easier to bear when shared with young people going through the same experiences.

The motivation for belonging influences how readily adolescents will give in to peer pressure and how much influence the group will have in their lives. In general, the more important it is to a teen to belong, the more susceptible he or she is to peer influence.

Interestingly, we now know that popular teens may be more susceptible to peer influence than previously thought because they work very hard to maintain their position at the top of the social pyramid. Part of this hard work may involve engaging in behav-

iors they think are expected of them, including smoking, drinking, or sexual activity.

A sense of self also is connected to identification with a particular group, like female, black, Jewish, Hispanic, gay or lesbian, etc. A few studies have found that a solid sense of belonging to one's ethnic group and its traditions—referred to as ethnic identity—is associated with many benefits, such as high self-esteem and high academic performance. Studies also find that a positive racial identity protects

African-American teenagers against the psychological or emotional harm of racial discrimination.

For racial and ethnic minority adolescents, positive experiences with their culture have to compete with negative media messages and experiences of discrimination. Even small talk can undermine positive ethnic and racial identity. For example, when asked where they are from, the answer "Maryland" or "California" is accepted from white and African-American teens. But Latino, Asian-American, and even Native-American teens may be asked a follow-up question—"No, where are you *really* from?"—causing them to feel like outsiders.

Parents and caring adults of the same racial or ethnic group can help promote positive racial and ethnic identity. Messages that emphasize ethnic pride, history, and traditions help promote positive identity. So, too, does exposing adolescents to books, music, movies, and stories related to their race, cultural heritage, and experience. Adoptive parents of children of another race or ethnicity may need to get outside support in helping their children develop a positive racial or ethnic identity.

Discussing discrimination openly with minority adolescents may be the best method for dealing with prejudice. When parents and caring adults speak forthrightly about discrimination, young people use more effective ways to cope with incidents of racial or ethnic bias, such as seeking outside support and direct problem-solving. Minority adolescents are more likely to use ineffective strategies—for example, engaging in verbal exchanges with the perpetrator—when parents do not talk openly with them about discrimination.

Parents report struggling to find a balance in preparing their children for discrimination: they want their children to learn how to protect them-

Show teens what makes a good friend

Good friends:

● Listen to each other

● Do not put each other down

● Do not intentionally hurt each other's feelings

● Can disagree without damaging each other

● Are dependable and trustworthy

● Express mutual respect

● Give each other room to change and grow

Glossary of sexual identity terms

SEXUAL ORIENTATION A person's emotional and sexual attraction to other people based on the gender of the other person. A person may identify their sexual orientation as heterosexual, lesbian, gay, bisexual, or queer.

GENDER IDENTITY A person's internal, deeply felt sense of being male, female, other, or in between. Everyone has a gender identity.

GENDER EXPRESSION OR GENDER PRESENTATION An individual's characteristics and behaviors that are perceived as masculine or feminine, such as appearance, dress, mannerisms, speech patterns, and social interactions.

HETEROSEXUAL OR STRAIGHT A person whose sexual and emotional feelings are mostly for people of the opposite sex.

HOMOSEXUAL OR GAY A person whose sexual and emotional feelings are mostly for people of the same sex.

LESBIAN A homosexual woman.

BISEXUAL A person whose sexual and emotional feelings are for males and females.

TRANSGENDER An umbrella term used to describe people whose gender identity, characteristics, or expression does not conform to the identity, characteristics, or expression traditionally associated with their biological sex.

LGBTQ An umbrella term that stands for "lesbian, gay, bisexual, transgender, and questioning." The category "questioning" is included to incorporate those who are not yet certain of their sexual orientation and/or gender identity.

QUEER Historically, a negative term used against people perceived to be LGBTQ, but more recently reclaimed by some people as a positive term describing all those who do not conform to traditional norms of gender and sexuality.

GENDER NON-CONFORMING A term used to describe a person who is or is perceived to have gender characteristics or behaviors that do not conform to traditional or societal expectations. Gender non-conforming people may or may not identify as LGBTQ.

SOURCE: *California Safe Schools Coalition.* Glossary of terms. Retrieved from http://www.casafeschools.org/resourceguide/glossary.html.

"I think trust plays a big part in friendship. If you can't trust your friends, how do you know that they aren't telling your secrets behind your back?"

Girl, 12

selves, without developing a general mistrust of people of other races. Immigrant parents who did not experience the United States as adolescents can find it particularly thorny to help their children deal with discrimination.

Examining intimacy: Am I lovable and loving?

Like anyone else, adolescents need to know they are loved by parents and other adults. They also need to be reassured that they are capable of giving and receiving affection in intimate friendships.

Many people, including teens, equate intimacy with sex. Intimacy and sex are not the same. Intimacy refers to close relationships in which people are open, honest, caring, and trusting. Intimacy usually is learned first with parents and within same-sex friendships, and that knowledge is later applied to romantic relationships. Young people who were raised in families where closeness is absent or where interpersonal relationships are distorted may have considerable difficulty learning and becoming comfortable with self-disclosure and self-expression, two building blocks of intimacy.

Friendships are the primary settings in which youth practice the intimacy skills involved in initiating, maintaining, and ending relationships. Within friendships, adolescents learn what it means to be trustworthy, honest, caring, and thoughtful with same-age peers, as well as how to avoid the ways of behaving that cause their friends to feel excluded or embarrassed. As teens "try on" new identities, friends provide valuable feedback.

During adolescence, parents often feel a loss of intimacy with their children. Throughout the teen years, intimacy with friends and romantic partners increases and eventually exceeds intimacy with parents. Adult caregivers should not interpret this natural transition to mean they are no longer central in their teenagers' lives. On the contrary, emotional support and guidance from adults remains crucial throughout adolescence.

Examining sexual identity: Who am I sexually?

The teen years mark the first time young people experience sexual feelings and are cognitively mature enough to think about their sexuality. Conse-

quently, adolescence is prime time for developing a sexual identity, the formation of which actually begins earlier in childhood.

All humans are sexual beings and develop a sexual identity. Sexual identity is one's identification with a gender and with a sexual orientation. Gender identity (masculine/feminine) may differ from a person's biological sex (male/female). Sexual orientation (heterosexual/bisexual/lesbian/gay) is based on an awareness of being attracted to the same or opposite sex. Sexual identity is not simply which of these categories a young person might find to be the best fit, but also how he or she identifies as a member of a social group. There is considerable diversity in combinations of gender identity and sexual orientation among humans.

As with all other areas of development, the process of forming a sexual identity can be uneven, out of sync, and therefore possibly confusing. How teens are educated about and exposed to sexuality influences how they feel about their sexual identity.

Adults can help by providing honest and accurate answers to young people about sex and sexual identity.

Adults must also take care not to label emerging sexual thoughts and behaviors as "perverted" or immoral. Adolescents may consider a wide range of sexual orientations or behaviors before establishing the sexual identity that will define them, and which they are comfortable expressing.

Experimentation and role-playing are common ways that adolescents will assume different sexual identities to see which fits. Romantic friendships, dating, and experimentation (including same-sex experimentation) are some ways adolescents determine their sexual identities and learn to express and receive sexual advances in ways that are in keeping with their values. Mid-to-late adolescence is a time when teens begin to become at ease with their changing bodies and sexual feelings.

The many facets of identity formation

During adolescence, young people grapple with how others see them and how they fit into the world. Identity formation is an iterative process, meaning that adolescents repeatedly try out different answers to the question, "Who am I?" At some points in the process they are firm in their resolve, and at other points they feel uncertain.

In forming an identity, adolescents may question their passions, values, and spiritual beliefs and also examine their relationships with family members, friends, romantic interests, and adults. They may think about their intrinsic gifts and talents and form a personal definition of success in school, at work, and in society at large. In addition to figuring out their place in the world, young people look inward at this time and often develop self-definitions based on body type, personality, gender, and culture.

Adolescent identity formation differs across contexts, because teenagers often see themselves one way when they are with parents and teachers and another way when they are with their peers. They can also see themselves and act differently within various peer groups. No matter what the context, adults can ease the process of self-definition by providing a safe and secure base from which young people can explore their identity.

Mental Health

The process of managing emotions

Emotions can bring discomfort for everyone, but this is especially true for adolescents, who are still learning to identify and manage their emotional responses. Emotional extremes are common during the teen years and may be reflected in mood swings, emotional outbursts, sadness, or behaviors intended to distract from uncomfortable feelings (such as sleeping or listening to loud music).

Teens, like all people, have some periods that are more challenging than others. For some, though, feelings of anxiety, sadness, anger, or stress may linger and become severe enough to interfere with their ability to function. It is estimated that at some point before age 20, one in 10 young people experiences a serious emotional disturbance that disrupts their ability to function at home, in school, or in the community. The good news is that most emotional disturbances are treatable.

Signs of emotional disturbance

What is considered normal and healthy behavior depends to some degree on culture. Serious disorders in one culture may not appear in another culture. The same is true across generations. One contemporary example is intentional self-injury (known as "cutting"), which is incomprehensible to many adults who are familiar with other types of emotional disturbances, such as depression or substance abuse.

A signpost of trouble to watch for is whether a teen's capacity to function in school, at home, and in relationships is being negatively affected by emotions or behaviors. Family and friends are usually the first people to notice.

Emotional disturbance follows no single pattern. Some adolescents suffer a single, prolonged episode in their teen years and enjoy good mental health in adulthood. Others experience emotional disturbances episodically, with bouts of suffering recurring in their later teen years and adulthood. Only a small percentage of adoles-

SIGNS OF DEPRESSION

- Frequent sadness, tearfulness, crying
- Decreased interest in activities or inability to enjoy formerly favorite activities
- Hopelessness
- Persistent boredom, low energy
- Social isolation, poor communication
- Extreme sensitivity to rejection or failure
- Increased irritability, anger, or hostility
- Difficulty with relationships

- Frequent complaints of physical illness such as headaches or stomachaches
- Frequent absences from school or poor performance in school
- Poor concentration
- Feeling overwhelmed easily or often
- A major change in eating and/or sleeping patterns
- Talk of or efforts to run away from home
- Thoughts or expressions of suicide or self-destructive behavior

SOURCE: *American Academy of Child and Adolescent Psychiatry.* (2008). The depressed child. Facts for Families. Retrieved from www.aacap.org/cs/root/facts_for_families/the_depressed_child.

SUICIDE

If a young person says he or she wants to kill him or herself, always take the statement seriously and immediately get help. If you think someone is suicidal, do not leave that person alone.

The suicide rate increases during the teen years and peaks in early adulthood (ages 20-24). There is a second peak in the suicide rate after age 65, and old age is when people are at highest risk. It is nearly impossible to predict who might attempt suicide, but some risk factors have been identified. These include depression or other mental disorders, a family history of suicide, family violence, and exposure to suicidal behavior of others, including media personalities. Opportunity also plays a role. Having a firearm in the home increases the risk.

The American Academy of Child and Adolescent Psychiatry recommends asking a young person whether she is depressed or thinking about suicide. They advise, "Rather than putting thoughts in the child's head, such a question will provide assurance that somebody cares and will give the young person the chance to talk about problems."

SOURCES: *American Academy of Child & Adolescent Psychiatry.* (2008). Teen suicide. Facts for Families. Retrieved June 4, 2009, from www.aacap.org/cs/root/facts_for_families/teen_suicide.

National Institute of Mental Health. (2009). Suicide in the U.S.: Statistics and prevention. Retrieved June 4, 2009, from www.nimh.nih.gov/health/publications/suicide-in-the-us-statistics-and-prevention/index.shtml.

cents who experience an episode of emotional disturbance will go on to have a lifelong disorder that seriously impairs their functioning as an adult.

The most common mental health disorders in adolescence are depression, characterized by prolonged periods of feeling hopeless and sad; anxiety disorders, which include extreme feelings of anxiety and fear; and alcohol and other drug abuse, including use of prescription drugs like Vicodin or Ritalin for non-medical reasons.

The underlying causes of emotional disturbances are varied and cannot always be identified. Many factors go into the mix, including genetic predisposition, environmental conditions such as exposure to lead or living in a chaotic household, and trauma such as abuse or witnessing a homicide.

Prolonged stress makes teens more vulnerable to emotional disturbances. A normal coping reaction to a difficult experience can impair someone's well-being if it goes on for too long. For example, if a teen is teased at school, it is normal—even if not desirable—for him or her to feel humiliated and anxious and to avoid the pain by skipping school, playing video games, or even experimenting with substances. These coping strategies can become harmful if chronic symptoms of anxiety or depression develop, or if behaviors such as overeating, self-injury ("cutting"), alcohol or other drug use—originally started to distract from uncomfort-able emotions—become compulsive or habitual.

Getting help

Most mental health disorders are treatable. Treatment often includes—and often works best—when multiple approaches are used. These can include cognitive-behavioral therapy, family therapy, medication, and supportive education for parents and other caring adults in how to provide stability and hope as the family navigates its way through the episode of emotional disturbance.

Parents of teens with Attention Deficit Hyperactivity Disorder (ADHD), however, have often experienced years of the frustration and exasperation that comes from trying to establish limits and discipline for children who seem consistently unable or unwilling to listen. Because all adolescents naturally strive toward assuming more responsibility and independence, the frustration of parenting a teen with ADHD may well intensify during this period of development.

A cycle of negative interaction, stress, and failure can also occur in the classroom between teachers and teens with ADHD. Teenagers who are disruptive, fidgety and impulsive can be singled out by the teacher, and labeled as disciplinary problems. Academic settings with multiple periods, large classes, teachers who have differing styles, and complex schedules present additional problems for the teenager with ADHD.

Professional help, especially help that is affordable, can be hard to find, as there is a shortage of trained mental health providers with expertise in adolescence. The sidebar in this section provides some resources where caring adults and teens can look for help.

The power of prevention

It is important to get involved early to teach positive coping skills and address environmental situations that may trigger emotional disturbances. The supports that bolster good mental health are the very same ones that promote healthy development in general. Especially valuable are opportunities for young people to practice identifying and naming emotions, to figure out coping skills that help them dissipate the energy of negative emotions, and to have the repeated, encouraging experience of being heard, understood, respected, and accepted.

RESOURCES

American Academy of Child and Adolescent Psychiatry: Facts for Families
Extensive series of briefs on a wide variety of behaviors and issues affecting families. http://www.aacap.org/cs/root/facts_for_families/facts_for_families

The Center for Mental Health in Schools: School Mental Health Project
Clearinghouse for resources on mental health in schools, including systemic, programmatic, and psychosocial/mental health concerns. http://smhp.psych.ucla.edu/

Surgeon General's Report on Mental Health
Includes a chapter on children and mental health. http://www.surgeongeneral.gov/library/mentalhealth/home.html

Technical Assistance Partnership for Child and Family Mental Health: Youth Involvement in Systems of Care. A Guide to Empowerment
Blueprints for local systems of care that are seeking to increase youth involvement. http://www.tapartnership.org/docs/Youth_Involvement.pdf

SOURCE: Whitlock, J., and Schantz, K. (2009). Mental illness and mental health in adolescence. *Research Facts and Findings.* ACT for Youth Center of Excellence. Retrieved June 3, 2009 from http://www.actforyouth.net/documents/MentalHealth_Dec08.pdf

SEXUALITY

CHAPTER 5

Understanding sexual development

SEXUALITY

"If someone wants to accept the consequences of sex, then it is their choice."

Girl, 15

Developing sexually is an expected and natural part of growing into adulthood. Most people have considered or experienced some form of sexual activity by the time they get out of their teens.

Research on adolescent sexuality concentrates on two areas—understanding healthy sexual development and investigating the risks associated with too-early or unsafe sexual activity.

Healthy sexual development involves more than sexual behavior. It is the combination of physical sexual maturation known as puberty, age-appropriate sexual behaviors, and the formation of a positive sexual identity and a sense of sexual well-being. During adolescence, teens strive to become comfortable with their changing bodies and to make healthy and safe decisions about what sexual activities, if any, they wish to engage in.

Expressions of sexual behavior differ among youth, and whether they engage in sexual activity depends on personal readiness, family standards, exposure to sexual abuse, peer pressure, religious values, internalized moral guidelines, and opportunity.

Motivations may include biological and hormonal urges, curiosity, and a desire for social acceptance. There is an added pressure today, especially with girls, to appear sexy in all contexts throughout their lives—school, leisure time, the workplace, with friends, in the community, and even while participating in sports or exercise.

Decisions to engage in, or limit, sexual activity in ways that are consistent with personal principles and protective of health reflect an adolescent's maturity and self-acceptance.

Healthy sexuality for everyone

Research shows that providing accurate, objective information to adolescents supports healthy sexual development.

All young people need to learn to be comfortable with their sexuality. This task may be especially challenging for teens who are gay, lesbian, bisexual, or transgender. These young people often feel worlds apart from their heterosexual peers, family, or members of their community, and they need support from adults more than ever. Parents and other caregivers may have difficulty providing straightforward information and advice to youth whose sexual orientations or practices diverge from those of the majority of the surrounding society.

Adults may find it helpful to keep in mind that sexual and other stages of development may be different for sexual-minority teens.

Regardless of how young people come to be gay, lesbian or bisexual, it is essential that these youth be loved and cared for during this time of exploring their sexual identity. Perhaps because of the stigma they face, sexual-minority youth are at higher risk than their heterosexual peers for substance abuse, early onset of intercourse, unintended

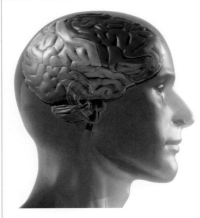

BRAIN BOX

Common folklore has often assumed that the "raging hormones" of adolescence are responsible for risky behaviors, including unsafe sex. The research, however, shows only small, direct effects of pubertal hormones (androgens and estrogens) on adolescent behavior. Rather, adolescent risk-taking appears to be due to a complex mix of genes, hormones, brain changes, and the environment. Hormones interact with changes occurring in the adolescent brain and in the adolescent's social world to affect adolescent behavior. In fact, psychological and social experiences have been shown to impact brain development and hormone levels, as well as the other way around.

SOURCE: Spear, L.P. (2008). The Psychobiology of Adolescence. In K.K. Kline (Ed.), *Authoritative Communities: The Scientific Case for Nurturing the Whole Child* (263–279). The Search Institute Series on Developmentally Attentive Community and Society (Vol. 5). New York: Springer.

pregnancy, HIV and other STIs, verbal and physical violence, and suicide.

Parents and caregivers of adolescents with disabilities, too, may not know how to respond to their child's sexual maturation and the changes

that come with puberty. Young people who live with physical, mental, or emotional disabilities will experience sexual development and must struggle with the same changes and choices of puberty that impact all human beings. This fact might be uncomfortable to some people, who may find it easier to view people with disabilities as "eternal children." In fact, youth with disabilities may need more guidance from adults, not less, because they may frequently feel isolated and quite different from their same-age peers.

Adolescents with disabilities may have some unique needs related to sex education. For example, children with developmental disabilities may learn at a slower rate than do their non-disabled peers; yet their physical maturation usually occurs at the same rate. As a result of the combination of normal physical maturation and slowed emotional and cognitive development, they may need sexual health information that helps build skills for appropriate language and behavior in public.

"I believe it is better to have sex while you are young."

Boy, 15

Sexual development through the teen years

The experience of adolescence is a dynamic mixture of physical and cognitive change coupled with social

More media, earlier first sexual activity

In a 2004 longitudinal study funded by the National Institutes of Health, early adolescents who had heavier sexual media diets of movies, music, television, and magazines were twice as likely as those with lighter sexual media diets to have initiated sexual intercourse by the time they were 16.

SOURCE: *The Media as Powerful Teen Sex Educators*, Jane D. Brown, University of North Carolina, March 2007

Will having sex
make me

popular?

How do
I deal with

pressure

to have sex?

WHAT
TEENS
MIGHT ASK

How do I
know I am
ready for

sex?

How
will I know
I'm in

love?

A person's **SEXUAL IDENTITY** is derived from emotional and sexual attraction to other people based on the other's gender. People may define their sexual identity as heterosexual, homosexual, gay, lesbian, or bisexual. **GENDER IDENTITY** describes a person's internal, deeply felt sense of being male, female, other, or in between. Everyone has a gender identity.

Sexual identity develops across a person's life span—different people might realize at different points in their lives that they are heterosexual, gay, lesbian, or bisexual. Adolescence is a period in which young people may still be uncertain of their sexual identity. Sexual behavior is not necessarily synonymous with sexual identity. Many adolescents—as well as many adults—may identify themselves as homosexual or bisexual without having had any sexual experience. Other people may have had sexual experiences with a person of the same sex but do not consider themselves to be gay, lesbian, or bisexual. This is particularly relevant during adolescence, a developmental stage marked by experimentation.

expectations, all of which impact sexual development. Hormone levels stimulate physical interest in sexual matters, and peer relationships shift toward more adult-style interactions. This section outlines the stages of sexual development.

Pre-adolescence (ages 6-10)
Sexual development begins well before adolescence. Hormonal changes—an elevation of androgens, estradiol, thyrotropin, and cortisol in the adrenal glands—start to emerge between the ages of 6 and 8.

The visible signs of puberty begin to show up between the ages of 9 and 12 for most children. Girls may grow breast buds and pubic and underarm hair as early as 8 or 9. In boys the growth of the penis and testicles usually begins between ages 10 and 11 but can start to occur at the age of 9.

Before age 10, children usually are not sexually active or preoccupied with sexual thoughts, but they are curious and may start to collect information and myths about sex from friends, schoolmates, and family members. Part of their interaction with peers may involve jokes and sex talk.

At this age, children become more self-conscious about their emerging sexual feelings and their bodies, and they are often reluctant to undress in front of others, even a parent of the same gender. Boys and girls tend to play with friends of the same gender and may explore sexuality with them, perhaps through touching. This does not necessarily relate to a child's sexual identity and is more about inquisitiveness than sexual preference.

Early adolescence (ages 11-13)
The passage into adolescence typically begins with the onset of menarche (menstruation) in girls and semenarche (ejaculation) in boys, both of which occur, on average, around age 12 or 13. For girls, menstruation starts approximately two years after breast buds—the first visible sign of puberty—develop, although it can happen anytime between ages 9 and 16.

Hormonal changes generated by the adrenals and testes in boys and the adrenals and ovaries in girls affect brain development. The impact of hormones on brain chemistry results in a larger amygdala in boys (the part of the brain governing emotions and instincts)

and a larger hippocampal area in girls (the section of the brain dealing with memory and spatial navigation). The adrenals can also pump some testosterone into girls and estrogen into boys, with 80 percent of boys experiencing temporary breast development during early adolescence.

As physical maturation continues, early adolescents may become alternately fascinated with and chagrined by their changing bodies, and often compare themselves to the development they notice in their peers. Sexual fantasy and masturbation episodes increase between the ages of 10 and 13. As far as social interactions go, many tend to be nonsexual—text messaging, phone calls, email—but by the age of 12 or 13, some young people may pair off and begin dating and experimenting with kissing, touching, and other physical contact, such as oral sex.

The vast majority of young adolescents are not prepared emotionally or physically for oral sex and sexual intercourse. If adolescents this young do have sex, they are highly vulnerable for sexual and emotional abuse, STIs, HIV, and early pregnancy.

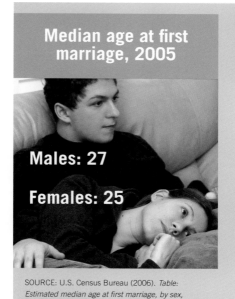

Median age at first marriage, 2005

Males: 27

Females: 25

SOURCE: U.S. Census Bureau (2006). *Table: Estimated median age at first marriage, by sex, 1890 to the present, from Current Population Survey, March and Annual Social and Economic Supplements, 2005 and earlier.* http://www.census.gov/population/socdemo/hh-fam/ms2.pdf

High school students who have had sexual intercourse

	1991	1995	2001	2007
Males	57%	54%	48%	50%
Females	51%	52%	43%	46%

SOURCE: Centers for Disease Control and Prevention (2008). *Youth risk behavior surveillance--United States 2007.* Surveillance Summaries, May 9, 2008. Morbidity & Mortality Weekly Report, http:apps.nccd.cdc.gov/yrbss

% ever had sexual intercourse by grade level, 2007

	9th grade	10th grade	11th grade	12th grade
Males	38.1%	45.6%	57.3%	62.8%
Females	27.4%	41.9%	53.6%	66.2%

SOURCE: Centers for Disease Control and Prevention (2007). *Youth risk behavior surveillance—United States, 2007.* Retrieved October 1, 2009 from http://apps.nccd.gov/yrbss

Middle adolescence (ages 14-16)

Testosterone in boys surges between the ages of 14 and 16, increasing muscle mass and setting off a growth spurt. Testosterone levels in boys are usually eight times greater than in girls, and this hormone is the strongest predictor of sexual drive, frequency of sexual thoughts, and behavior.

Middle adolescents exhibit an increased interest in romantic and sexual relationships. The sexual behavior during this time tends to be exploring, with strong erotic interest. Sexual activity at this age varies widely and includes the choice not to have sex.

At this age, both genders experience a high level of sexual energy, although boys may have a stronger sex drive due to higher testosterone levels. Sex drive, commonly known as libido, refers to sexual desire or an interest in engaging in sex with a partner.

On an abstract level, adolescents ages 14 to 16 understand the consequences of unprotected sex and teen parenthood, if properly taught, but cognitively they may lack the skills to integrate this knowledge into everyday situations or consistently to act responsibly in the heat of the moment.

Before the age of 17, many adolescents have willingly experienced sexual intercourse. Teens who have early sexual intercourse report strong peer pressure as a reason behind their decision. Some adolescents are just curious about sex and want to experience it.

No matter what the motivation, many teens say they regret having had sex as early as they did, even if the activity was consensual. Research published in the journal *Pediatrics* noted that up to one-half of the sexually experienced teenagers in the 2007 study said they felt "used," guilty, or regretful after having sex. The findings indicated that girls were twice as likely as boys to respond that they "felt bad about themselves" after having sex, and three times more likely to say they felt "used."

Masturbation

Masturbation is sexual self-stimulation, usually achieved by touching, stroking, or massaging the male or female genitals until this triggers an orgasm. Masturbation is very ordinary—even young children have been known to engage in this behavior. As the bodies of children mature, powerful sexual feelings begin to develop, and masturbation helps release sexual tension. For adolescents, masturbation is a common way to explore their erotic potential, and this behavior can continue throughout adult life.

Sexual fantasies

Sexual fantasies are usually associated with masturbation, but the two can occur independently. Sexual daydreams and fantasies are common—most people have them, not just teenagers and not just boys.

Fantasies often differ between the sexes. Sexual aggression and dominance are recurring themes in young male fantasies and usually contain very specific and graphic sexual behaviors but little emotional involvement. For adolescent females, sexual fantasies often involve relating to others, and they are more likely to involve sexual activities with which the girl is already familiar. A teenage girl's fantasies also are typically about someone they know—a boyfriend, TV or music stars, friends, casual acquaintances.

The important thing to tell teenagers about sexual fantasies is that thoughts, in and of themselves, are not sick, weird, or wrong. They are just that: thoughts. Making a teenager feel guilty or ashamed or suggesting that their dreams reveal psychological problems can lead to their feeling at odds with their sexuality. It can also make them more vulnerable to becoming obsessed about a particular sexual fantasy.

"I hear my friends talking about their sex lives, but I don't really care because I am not having sex, so getting information about sex doesn't matter to me."

Girl, 14

Romantic versus sexual relationships

Libido is distinct from romantic interest, which may or may not be sexual in nature. Romantic interest usually emphasizes emotions—love, intimacy, compassion, appreciation—rather than the pursuit of physical pleasure driven by libido.

We may see romance as a feminine tendency, but recent studies indicate that teenage boys are as romantic as girls—a finding that runs counter to the stereotype of adolescent males as "players." Peggy Giordano, a sociology professor at Bowling Green University, conducted interviews with a random sample of 1,316 boys and girls drawn from the seventh, ninth, and 11th grades and found that boys were at least as emotionally invested in their romantic relationships as their partners were.

Both boys and girls in the study agreed, however, that girls in heterosexual romantic relationships hold the power in the decision of when to have sexual intercourse.

Late adolescence (ages 17-19)
By the time an adolescent is 17, sexual maturation is typically complete, although late bloomers are not uncommon. Sexual behavior during this time may be more expressive, since cognitive development in older adolescents has progressed to the point where they have somewhat greater impulse control and are capable of intimate and sharing relationships.

Intimate relationships usually involve more than sexual interest.

Emotionally, falling in love is powerful and all-consuming, and it involves a greater portion of the adolescent brain.

Brain scientists at University College London scanned the brains of young lovers while they were thinking about their boyfriends and girlfriends and discovered that four separate areas of the brain became very active. This affirms the notion that falling in love is an all-encompassing emotion that engages nearly every part of the mind and body.

What works at what age

EARLY TEEN YEARS (AGES 11-14)
Young teens tend to be concrete and short-term in their thinking, and often do not consider long-term consequences when making decisions. This is a good time to talk about delaying sexual activity but a bad time to hammer home long-term benefits or consequences.

MIDDLE TEEN YEARS (15-17)
Risk peaks during these years, and teens of this age question limits and authority. Scare tactics do not work at this age; rather, emphasize the influence of peers. Talking about how to handle peer pressure and changing social circles (about being associated with certain cliques or groups, and about how hanging around with older and younger teens affects sexual behavior and risk-taking) works best at this age.

LATE TEEN YEARS (17 AND OLDER)
Older adolescents are entering new social situations such as work and college, so talking about sexual behavior in the context of wider relationships can be helpful. For example, one might talk about how sexual behavior helps form a personal identity or define young people, both in how they may see themselves and how they are viewed within an intimate relationship, in their community, or in various peer groups.

Ways teens protect their sexual health

Delaying sexual intercourse is associated with many positive outcomes: less regret about the timing of one's first sexual experience, fewer sexual partners, and a decreased likelihood of being involved in coercive sexual relationships.

Waiting to have sex until one is in a respectful, loving relationship protects a young person's emotional well-being, too. Today's teenagers are postponing their first sexual activity, as compared to young people from prior decades. The proportion of teenagers who reported having sexual intercourse rose steadily through the 1970s and '80s, fueling a sharp rise in teen pregnancy. The trend reversed around 1991 as a result of AIDS, changing sexual mores, and other factors. In 2007 nearly half (48 percent) of high school students ages 15 to 19 reported to the CDC they had had sexual intercourse. This was a minor increase since 2005, but the good news is that teens are initiating sex at older ages today than their counterparts in the 1990s. They

also are reporting having fewer sexual partners than high school students in 1991 had.

Sex with multiple partners is not widespread among teenagers. Only 15 percent of adolescents have had sexual intercourse with four or more people during their lives. Teenagers with multiple sex partners are more likely to contract an STI, compared with teenagers who have only one sex partner.

Among those who are sexually active, the majority use contraception. The preferred method of contraception

is condoms, although condom use in teens showed a slight drop between 2005 and 2007, from 63 percent to 61 percent who reported having used a condom the last time they had sex.

The younger a teen is at first sex, the less likely is the use of a condom or another form of contraception. Condoms protect teens from sexually transmitted infections and pregnancies when they are used correctly and consistently. Other hormonal forms of contraception for girls like the oral contraceptive pills, the patch, the

Talking to teens about sex

For parents and teens both, talking about sex can be uncomfortable. Teens do not want to see their parents in a sexual light, and parents often do not want to see their children that way, either. That said, teens still report that their parents are the greatest influences on their sexual behavior, and research backs them up. Guidelines for successful teen-parent conversation about sex include the following:

- Engage children in open, honest discussions regarding appropriate dating behavior, emotional and sexual intimacy, sexual identity, and emotional commitment.
- Discuss responsibilities regarding commitment and intimacy in romantic relationships.
- Discuss responsibilities regarding avoiding pregnancy, STIs, and HIV.
- Teach teens not to exploit other people socially, emotionally, or sexually. This is impossible to teach if it is not also modeled. Similarly, teach teens how to recognize abusive and exploitive relationships.
- Set appropriate limits regarding dating, such as the age at which dating will be allowed, curfews, and the age of person your child may date.
- Since teens may be embarrassed to talk with their parents about sex and relationships, try to provide access to other trusted adults (church members, counselors, relatives, etc.)
- Be open to questions and values expressed by the teen.

SOURCE: Beeler, N., Patrick, B., Pedon, S. Normal child sexual development and promoting healthy sexual development. *The Institute for Human Services for the Pennsylvania Child Welfare Training Program 203: Sexuality of Children: Healthy Sexual Behaviors and Behaviors Which Cause Concern.* Handout 3-1. Available at: http://www.pacwcbt.pitt.edu/Curriculum/203%20Sexuality%20of%20Children%20Healthy%20Sexual%20Behaviors%20and/Handouts/HO%203-1.pdf

> ## "It's all right for a person to have sex when they are ready mentally, physically, and emotionally. It is not all right for someone younger than me to have sex."
>
> *Girl, 15*

injection (Depo-Provera) or the vaginal ring provide higher levels of protection from unintended pregnancies but no protection from sexually transmitted infections (an excellent chart comparing contraceptive methods can be found at www.seasonique.com). When teens become sexually active, ideally, the male partner would use a condom and the female would use a hormonal method of contraception to get double protection. Fewer than one quarter of teens, however, currently do this.

When unprotected sex has already happened, emergency contraception can be used by girls to prevent pregnancy, especially if it is obtained within 72 hours of having sex. Known as Plan B, this concentrated dose of the hormone found in birth control pills is available over the counter in pharmacies for young women ages 17 or older. It is available for younger girls by prescription.

Risky consequences

Early and unsafe sexual activity can result in unintended teenage pregnancy and sexually transmitted infections (STIs).

Research shows that giving birth before age 18 limits the future for both the girl and her baby. Girls who become mothers early are less likely to complete high school and more likely to face poverty as an adult than other teens. Teenage girls who are pregnant often do not get sufficient prenatal care, and are more prone to high blood pressure and preeclampsia, a dangerous medical condition, than pregnant women in their 20s and 30s. Teens also are at greater risk for postpartum depression and having low–birth-weight babies (under five pounds). Low–birth- weight babies can have many medical problems, such as breathing difficulties, as well as developmental or growth delays. In addition, children of teen mothers can experience other health problems and higher rates of abuse or neglect; they are also likely to live in poverty and to receive inadequate health care compared to children born to mothers aged 18 and over.

For more than a decade, rates of teen pregnancy and birth in the U.S. were down from an all-time peak of 61.8 births per thousand in 1991. This decline has leveled off, and the teen birth rate rose slightly between 2005 and 2007. This translates to about 20,000 more births to teenagers in 2006 compared to the year before. Births have risen slightly among women between the ages of 20 and 24 as well.

Sexually transmitted infections are also a major concern. Sex without condoms puts young people at risk for STIs, including HIV infection. Adolescent cases account for half of all STIs. The latest Centers for Disease Control and Prevention (CDC) statistics tell us that more than 3 million teenage girls in America have an STI. In a national study in 2003, teens aged 14 to 19 were tested for four infections: Human Papillomavirus (HPV), chlamydia, trichomoniasis, and herpes simplex virus. While one-quarter of the girls overall had at least one of these infections, nearly half of the African-American girls were infected.

The most common STI found in teen girls ages 14 to 19 is HPV, which can cause genital warts in women and men and is usually not a serious condi-

"I get my information about sex from my friends and magazines." *Girl, 16*

tion. Some HPV viruses can lead to cervical cancer later in life. Fortunately, a vaccine targeting HPV recently became available, and national health organizations recommend the vaccine for 11- and 12-year-old girls, and catch-up shots for females ages 13 to

26. Vaccines for boys are being readied but they are not yet recommended.

Chlamydia, another very common infection, can cause pelvic inflammatory disease and infertility. This infection is caused by bacteria and can be easily treated if it is detected. However, many youth with the infection do not have any symptoms and are unaware that they have it. In pregnancy, chlamydia and HIV can infect the growing baby. If these infections are transmitted to babies, they can cause low birth weight, eye

Keeping a cool head on a hot topic

- **Get your zen on**
  When young people bring up sex, try to be calm and reasonable, no matter what the situation. Anger, surprise, and embarrassment are not proper responses, even if your teen is trying to provoke you.

- **Tone is everything**
  Teens may have fears that their sexual thoughts and urges are unnatural or make them freaks. Reassure teens that sexual thoughts and expressions are normal, and it is OK to have these feelings without acting on them.

- **Papa, don't preach**
  Phrases like "But you're only 16!" are not helpful. Teens are looking for someone to listen and to give accurate information about sex, not deliver sermons or make them feel guilty or ashamed.

infection, pneumonia, blood infection, brain damage, lack of coordination in body movements, blindness, deafness, acute hepatitis, meningitis, liver disease, cirrhosis, or stillbirth.

What adults can do

Young people care about what their parents and other important adults in their lives think. When teens—both boys and girls—believe their parents want them to delay having sex, they are more likely to defer first intercourse. When there is a warm relationship, adolescents are even more apt to behave the way their parents wish them to, which often means postponing sexual activity.

Parents and caring adults can foster closeness with their teens and increase the odds of their avoiding risky sexual behavior by establishing an environment in which young people can feel comfortable and respected talking or asking about sexual matters. Clear rules about dating, curfews, and whether adolescents may be alone together in the teen's bedroom are also important but should be negotiated so that they are perceived as fair by the teen.

Parents and those who work with adolescents need to educate themselves about the various factors affecting sexual development. Physical changes make teens appear ready for sexual activities they might not be prepared for emotionally and cognitively. Poor communication about sex, limited or inaccurate information, media influences, and negative attitudes also can impact a young person's sexual health and identity.

An essential way an adult can influence sexual behavior is by being a source of accurate information. Teens need straight talk about how to refuse to have sex if they do not want to have it. They also need to be shown the right way to use condoms. Adult involvement in this regard is more important than ever: 47 percent of teens say their parents are the most important influence in their decisions about sex, and younger teens view parents as even more important. If teenagers cannot get information from their parents or caring adults, they typically will rely on friends and the media, especially the Internet, to answer questions about sexual health.

Sometimes adults wonder how much information is too much. Researchers have found no evidence that either talking about contraception or making contraception available to teens hastens the onset of first sex.

Sex education and social influences

According to the 2002 National Survey of Family Growth (NSFG), only 2 percent of adolescents say they are getting essential information about contraception, sexual safety, and other matters. Research actually suggests that young people who are knowledgeable about sexuality and reproductive health are less likely to engage in early sexual activity or unprotected sex.

Schools do not necessarily provide complete or accurate information to educate adolescents about sexual health and sexuality. Abstinence-only sex education curricula and programs have

been widespread in American schools. A recent evaluation of several abstinence-only sex education curricula, which teach young people to postpone sexual intercourse until marriage and include no information about contraception, has shown them to be ineffective. The researchers from Mathematica, Inc. who conducted the evaluation found that the children who took part in sexual-abstinence education classes engaged in sexual intercourse for the first time at the same age as children who did not receive these classes.

The participating students also did not gain more awareness of the dangers of unprotected sex than did their non-participating counterparts.

Adults can expand on what is taught in the classroom by welcoming discussions about sexual behavior and risks, relationships, emotions, and sexual urges. This kind of respectful, in-depth communication can positively affect a young person's sexual development.

Sexuality is a vital part of growing up

During adolescence, teens learn how to deal with sexual feelings, experience sexual fantasies, and perhaps enjoy romantic relationships. They may choose to delay sexual activity, or not have sex at all, which falls within the spectrum of normal adolescent behavior.

These choices are all part of sexuality. Healthy sexual development is not simply a matter of sex but involves a young person's ability to manage intimate and reproductive behavior responsibly and without guilt, fear, or shame.

American teenagers grow up in a culture in which sex informs everything from the type of clothes they wear and the music they listen to, to the images and messages they continually absorb through the media.

Helping adolescents separate truth from hype and recognize all aspects of sexual development encourages them to make informed and healthy decisions about sexual matters.

10 ways TEENS can express LOVE without SEX

Make a handmade gift

Read to **each** other

Contribute or volunteer for a cause he or she cares about

Offer to do a chore

Bake a heart-shaped dessert

Program their I-Pod or make a CD with songs that are **special** to both

Send a **loving** text message

Write a **poem** *or a love letter*

Go through the car wash **together**

Rent a **romantic** movie

SPIRITUALITY & RELIGION

CHAPTER 6

Faith is a factor in exploring identity

"The best thing about my religion is that everyone in the community is nice and accepts your flaws."

Girl, 12

During adolescence, young people begin to ponder larger life questions, such as why there is good and evil and what it means to be human. The answers to these questions lie within the realm of spirituality.

Spirituality centers on the connection to a reality greater than oneself and can include the sacred experience of religious awe and reverence. Spirituality involves deep feelings and beliefs, including a person's sense of purpose, connection to others, and understanding of the meaning of life.

Religion, on the other hand, is a set of common beliefs and practices shared by a group of people. It can encompass cultural or ancestral traditions, writings, history, and mythology, as well as personal faith and mystical experience.

Spiritual development is shaped both within and outside of religious traditions, beliefs, and practices. Adolescents distinguish between religion and spirituality. In a nationally representative survey conducted as a part of the National Study of Youth and Religion (NSYR) in 2002 and 2003, 55 percent of adolescents ages 13 to 17 said that the description "spiritual but not religious" was somewhat true or very true of them.

Most adolescents say they believe in God. The NSYR found that 84 percent of adolescents ages 13 to 17 reported believing in God, and 65 percent reported praying at least once a week.

In the same study, 85 percent of teens reported being affiliated with a religious denomination or tradition, and 42 percent reported attending religious service at least once a week. Thirty-nine percent reported participating in a youth group. Just over half (52 percent) said their religious faith was very or extremely important in shaping their daily life.

Developing a spiritual outlook

Theology professor James W. Fowler describes adolescence as the stage during which young people begin to form their own spiritual identity and outlook. Typically, children in early adolescence do not yet have a sufficiently developed sense of reason upon which to construct independent views about religion and spirituality. They are still guided by their parents or other adults as well as influenced by peers.

As they grow older, teens develop an understanding of the unknown and

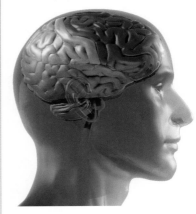

BRAIN BOX

Prayer and meditation appear to stimulate those parts of the brain responsible for mental focus and higher thinking and reasoning skills. A 2003 study using positron emission tomography (PET) and functional magnetic resonance imaging (fMRI) found that when nuns performed a meditative prayer for almost an hour, during which time they focused on a phrase from the Bible or prayer, there was increased blood flow to the areas of the brain that together regulate and focus attention.

SOURCE: Newberg, A., Pourdehnad, M., Alavi, A., and D'Aquili, E.G. (2003). Cerebral blood flow during meditative prayer: Preliminary findings and methodological issues. *Perceptual and Motor Skills*, 97, 625–630.

unknowable. Adolescence can be a time of intense religious and spiritual questioning for many young people. This might be because the development of more complex cognitive abilities promotes thinking on the existential level as well as the formation of a broader world view.

In the U.S., where personal religious freedom is allowed, adolescents might struggle with whether or not to hold on to the religion of their

> "I practice the same religion I did when I was a child, because that's what I was raised on. When I got older, I understood the real reasons behind the beliefs."
>
> *Boy, 15*

Who attends religious services more often?

YOUNGER TEENS In 2006, 42 percent of eighth graders said they attended religious services at least once a week. As teens got older, fewer attended every week (36 percent of 10th graders and 32 percent of 12th graders). Interestingly, older adolescents as a group do not consider themselves to have become less religious, which suggests that for older adolescents, religiosity extends well beyond attendance at religious services.

AFRICAN-AMERICAN TEENS In 12th grade, 44 percent of African-American students attended religious services at least once a week, compared to 31 percent of white students.

WEALTHIER TEENS In 12th grade, students whose parents had graduated from college (an indicator of higher income) were more likely to attend religious services than students whose parents' education ended with high school (38 percent vs. 28 percent).

SOURCE: *Child Trends* analysis of Monitoring the Future Survey data, 1976 to 2006. www.childtrendsdatabank.org/pdf/32_PDF.pdf

childhood. Some adolescents may want to explore other faiths or spiritual disciplines in a quest to find one that is personally meaningful to them. In the U.S., adolescence is the most common time for a switch in religious affiliation.

However, for many cultural groups, religion is intricately intertwined with ethnic and national identity. Adolescents in these cultures typically do not change religions, with no detriment to their development.

Young people can become more religious than their parents, and young people who hold deeper religious beliefs than their parents report more positive family relations. The opposite tends to be true when parents are more religious than their adolescent children.

Faith participation can shield teens from risky behaviors

There has been surprisingly little scientific research on the impact of religion and spirituality on young people, but the research that does exist suggests that faith-based organizations can provide young people with role models, moral direction, spiritual experiences, positive social and organizational ties, and community and leadership skills.

Attendance at religious services and ceremonies, public prayer, and participation in group religious activities, including youth groups, is associated with less cigarette, alcohol, and marijuana use; higher self-esteem; and more positive family relationships. Attending religious services may also affect performance in school. Strong religious communities emphasize and reward socially acceptable behavior and encourage young people to keep up their studies.

> ## "My faith pushes me to be the best I can be."
> *Girl, 12*

Ways to promote spiritual development

- **SUPPORT** young people's commitment to social justice. By reaching out to others and trying to right wrongs, a young person can experience a deepening of personal faith.

- **WORK** with religious-based youth groups to provide supervised activities geared to teens' interests and needs. These could be drop-in centers, musical programs and dances, or late-night programs.

- **ALLOW** youth to express their religious faith and spirituality and facilitate their search for better understanding of the tradition in which they were raised or of other religions or spiritual practices.

- **POLL** the youth in your place of worship on their issues and concerns and set up discussion groups between teens and adults.

- **BUILD** relationships between adults and teens through intergenerational programs, religious services, retreats, and social activities at your place of worship. These opportunities provide positive role models for adolescents and also help dispel adults' myths and fears about young people.

- **ENCOURAGE** exposure to, and creative expressions in, art, music, literature, dance, and theater.

- **VISIT** local art museums with youth to view religious paintings and sculptures. Many churches and places of worship also offer tours and talks about distinctive artwork and the spiritual meanings of architectural features.

> **"I questioned my faith sometimes because when I would go to church people would shout and get the Holy Ghost, and I never got it. I thought it was because I didn't believe enough."**
>
> *Girl, 14*

Being involved in a religious or spiritual community affords a young person access to positive adult role models and social support systems of fellow worshipers. Nearly half (48 percent) of adolescent respondents to the 2002 NSYR survey believed that their religious congregation was a very good place to go for help with serious problems, and 26 percent said it was a fairly good place to go for help.

The private practice of religion—defined as personal prayer, individual study of religious texts, and personal importance of religion in one's life—does not protect against habitual or regular involvement in risky behaviors to the same degree as does social participation in a religious community. This may be especially true for smoking, which is highly addictive.

We still have much to learn about how young people's personal religious commitment and the private practice of their faith affect other aspects of adolescents' well-being.

Religion is not always a sanctuary

While organized religion fosters a sense of belonging for the majority of young people, it can also lead to a painful rejection of those who are perceived not to belong, such as gay, lesbian, and other sexual-minority youth.

Some major religious groups maintain that same-sex attraction is against sacred teachings and that practicing anything other than a heterosexual lifestyle is sinful or unnatural.

Some religious groups close their doors to homosexuals or try to persuade sexual-minority youth to change their sexual orientation though therapy. Some religious groups also become involved in political advocacy to ensure that laws and public policies regarding sexual orientation are consistent with their religious doctrine.

Religious-based intolerance can limit the ability of sexual-minority youth to receive the full benefit of religious connection and can also cause deep psychological and emotional anguish. Religious adults and faith-based organizations can help by focusing on and building a relationship with the adolescent as a whole person.

Adolescence: A time of questioning and belonging

Spiritual development and religion can offer a positive environment for youth, giving them a sense of belonging and beneficial relationships with peers and adults, as well as providing a sense of meaning and purpose.

Spiritual development is shaped both within and outside of religious traditions, beliefs, and practices. This development leads to searching, which results in some young people enriching their faith and others diverging from the religious traditions they grew up with.

> **"I spent some time away from my religion and realized it was important to me."**
>
> *Boy, 18*

JAMES FOWLER'S

STAGES of FAITH

James W. Fowler, professor emeritus of theology and human development at Emory University, has written extensively about spiritual development across the lifespan. He describes the cognitive, emotional, and behavioral dimensions of faith development at different life stages.

1 Intuitive-protective faith ages 3 to 7

Children at this age have no inner structures for sorting and understanding their experiences. Their lives are a seamless world of fantasy, stories, experiences, and imagery. These images include the real events of daily life and the imaginary life of the child. Children's faith is influenced by the examples, stories, and actions of others, especially of adults with authority. Fowler claims the strength of this stage of faith lies in the birth of the imagination and the ability to hold the intuitive understandings and feelings in powerful images and stories. The pitfalls of this stage of faith lie in the potential for the child to be overwhelmed by images of terror and destructiveness. The transition to the next spiritual stage involves the child's growing concern to clarify what is real and what only seems that way.

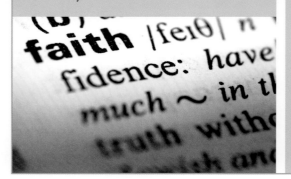

2 Mythic-literal faith elementary school age

To move to this second stage, children will necessarily have progressed to the developmental level of concrete operational thinking. The world has now become linear, orderly, and predictable; faith at this stage becomes a matter of reliance on the stories, rules, and implicit values of the family's faith community.

During this spiritual stage, the child begins to accept the stories and beliefs that symbolize belonging to his or her community. The child typically makes strong associations with "people like us" and tends to look critically at those who are "different." Stories are taken as literal in their meaning.

3 Synthetic-conventional faith adolescence

The term "synthetic" here means that the adolescent attempts to draw together the disparate elements of his or her life into an integrated identity. The term "conventional" indicates that the spiritual values and beliefs the adolescent holds are derived from other people who play significant roles in his or her life and, for the most part, are accepted at face value.

Young people at this stage do not have a sure enough grasp of their own identity and faith, nor sufficiently developed judgment to construct an independent perspective. Also, they are acutely attuned to the expectations and judgments of others. As a result, a young person at this stage may hold deep spiritual convictions, yet has not examined them critically.

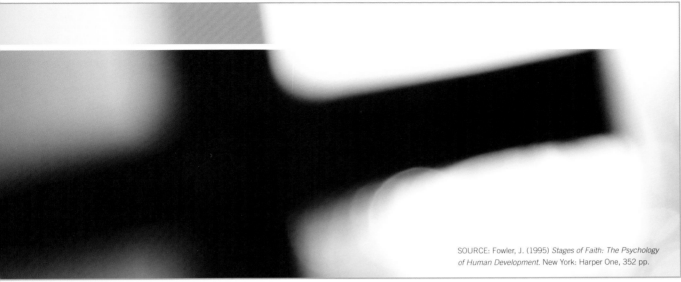

SOURCE: Fowler, J. (1995) *Stages of Faith: The Psychology of Human Development*. New York: Harper One, 352 pp.

④ Individuative-reflective faith
late adolescence and young adulthood

During this stage the individual emerges from the encircling influence of significant others. Young people begin to hold themselves, and others, more accountable for their own "authenticity, congruence, and consistency." They are eager to take responsibility for their beliefs, actions, and decisions and will no longer tolerate just following the crowd.

Young people at this stage do not sit easily with a leadership structure that requires them to be dependent upon it. They want leadership that acknowledges and respects their personal positions and allows room for them to contribute to the decision-making of the group.

⑤ Conjunctive faith
adulthood and midlife

The experience of reaching midlife can lead to a new stage of faith development. This transition coincides with a realization of the power and reality of death; feelings of growing and looking older; one's children's reaching teenage or adult years; and the awareness that there are aspects of one's own identity and circumstances that cannot be changed. Fowler sums up the life experience needed to begin to transition into this stage as "having learnt by having our noses rubbed in our finitude." Conjunctive faith accepts paradox and the apparent contradictions of perspectives on truth as intrinsic to that truth. People at this stage will "resist reductionist interpretations and are generally prepared to live with ambiguity, mystery, wonder, and apparent irrationalities."

⑥ Universalizing
midlife and beyond

Only rarely do people reach this stage of faith development. Fowler's examples include Mother Teresa and Mahatma Gandhi, who are characterized as selfless. They have given up ego for the greater good of the community.

PROFILES OF DEVELOPMENT

CHAPTER 7

Out of sync is completely normal

Adolescent growth and development do not move along on a seamless, never-wavering path. Cognitive development can spurt ahead of physical changes, and vice-versa. Similarly, cognitive and physical development may be in sync, but social development might be delayed.

The following profiles show how teenagers' unique patterns of physical growth and cognitive development can have emotional and social significance.

You will no doubt recognize some of these young people; you might have fit one of these descriptions yourself when you were an adolescent. Having teenagers read the profiles may help them see that their nonlinear development is completely normal and to be expected.

They may even gain some insights on how to handle certain situations.

How to handle the unique patterns of teen growth

Physical, cognitive, and social development typically are not in sync all the way through adolescence. Early and late bloomers in the physical sense are acutely aware of being out of sync with their peers, and reassurance that they will catch up—or that other teens will catch up with them—can be extremely helpful. Also helpful is playing the "mean mom" or "mean dad" role and limiting their exposure to situations they are not ready to handle.

When delays are cognitive or social, it is easier to blame the ado-

lescent and expect him or her to fix it—whether that means improving in social graces, being more organized and on time, or being more thoughtful about others' feelings.

It is important for adults to follow the same strategies they use for physical development that is out of sync: reassure both themselves and their teen that it is normal, and put in place strategies to help social and cognitive skills develop. These strategies include allowing an extra 15 minutes in the morning to get organized, spending extra time practicing "what if" scenarios, and putting in place systems of accountability. Of course, if any delays seem extreme, professional help should be sought.

CHAPTER 7 PROFILES OF DEVELOPMENT | 79

Ever since she can remember, people have been telling Sara she could be a movie star. She is extremely pretty, exuding innocence and simplicity. At the age of 11 she began her menstrual periods, and by her 13th birthday she had the fully developed breasts and rounded hips of a much older teenager. Sara was at first delighted by all the attention, since seemingly overnight she had become the envy of many girls her age, not to mention popular with older boys, who previously thought of her as just a kid. She begged her mother to let her date high school boys, but then became petrified and overwhelmed when they tried to kiss her and touch her body. If the attention from the guys at school wasn't confusing enough, older men—guys practically as old as her uncles, eeeuuuu!—are always making remarks about her looks, as if all of a sudden she had become public property. She has become so embarrassed about her body that she has stopped hanging out with her girlfriends, preferring to hide out in her room. When Sara goes out in public, she wears baggy sweatshirts and jeans and hunches her shoulders in an effort to hide her shape. She never makes eye contact—"What's the point," she thinks, "No one looks at me above chest-level, anyway."

SARA AND MICHAEL illustrate some of the challenges of early bloomers. They are physically quite mature, to the point where people are not recognizing them for who they are—still children. Even though they have the bodies of adults, they are nowhere near emotionally ready to be sexually active. Michael's physical maturity has resulted in his hanging out with an older age group, which has led to experimenting with sex, drugs, and alcohol and other risk-taking behaviors he is not emotionally prepared to handle. Sara has responded to her early physical development by withdrawing socially. Her mother, or a caring adult, could assist Sara by not allowing her to

MICHAEL

More than six feet tall, handsome, and with six-pack abs, 15-year-old Michael looks like the next teen idol. He excels at athletics and everybody wants him on their team. He is popular and well-liked, which makes his parents happy. Playing sports means hanging out with juniors and seniors, who invite him to parties where there is drinking and where sometimes drugs are passed around. Older girls—jeez, some of them you could call women!—pay attention to him too, and seem much more interested in his body than in anything he has to say. But inside, Michael feels anything but mature and confident. Even though it is exciting to be included in these parties, he doesn't feel ready to experiment with drugs and alcohol. Yet, he can't figure out how to stand up for himself and say, "No thanks." Sex is the same way—Michael is flattered being hit on by older girls, which is every guy's dream, right? Yet, he also feels weirded out by the pressure to be sexual, and worried the girls will laugh at his reluctance. Michael doesn't know how to put his feelings into words, so he usually goes along with it but feels confused afterward. Sometimes, Michael wishes people could see the kid he is inside, rather than just the man standing before them.

date older boys, even though this might make Sara unhappy in the moment. Similarly, Michael's parents could take some of the pressure off their son by not allowing him to attend lots of parties with older team members and their friends. They can also discuss ways in which Michael can say no and gracefully sidestep uncomfortable or dangerous situations. Sara and Michael could also benefit by being encouraged to be friends with more boys and girls their own age, and to get involved in activities that do not put undue emphasis on physical appearance.

TOMAS

Tomas was the undisputed king of middle school—smart, outgoing, the kind of guy both girls and boys felt comfortable around. Everything changed in high school. Most of the other guys his age seem stronger, more muscular, and more attractive—they are 16 going on manly. Big and athletic, they knock him over during football practice and run right by him on the basketball court as if he were invisible. He still has some buddies from middle school, but even they cannot help with the feelings of physical inadequacy he experiences on and off the field. While Tomas continues to get good grades, he sometimes feels reluctant to raise his hand or participate much in class because he doesn't want to draw attention to his small stature. After practice and in class, the other boys talk easily to the girls, but Tomas doesn't feel like he has a chance. The girls seem intimidating, too—tall and as confident as supermodels. When he looks in the mirror, a little boy stares back at him.

Physically, **TOMAS AND LESLIE** are late bloomers. Even though it is difficult not to be as tall and muscular as the other boys, Tomas is clearly on track in other areas and is emotionally ready for more mature relationships. He may be socially reticent at times, but he has the ability to be liked by his peers. Adults can support him by affirming that his physical development is normal and that he will catch up soon enough. Also, cheering on his efforts to shine academically will help to sustain his optimism.

LESLIE

At 15, Leslie is small and wiry, with a boyish frame and a childlike face. Looking at Leslie, people might mistake her for a 12-year-old, but then she opens her mouth and all bets are off. Leslie is bright and studious, a complex thinker who tosses around ideas and concepts as if they are hacky sacks. Leslie doesn't think about her body size much, preferring the life of the mind. She has expanded her world view beyond the bathroom mirror and is involved in a variety of causes near and dear to her heart, like the environment and animal rescue. In middle school, Leslie was intimidated by being short and petite and hid her light under a bushel. But in high school her perspective shifts and centers on learning and getting into a good college so she can pursue her dream of becoming a veterinarian.

LESLIE is a good example of someone who is extremely mature in the academic and emotional realms. Her future-thinking and planning skills are perhaps better developed than many of her peers'. Cognitively, she is way ahead, but physically Leslie is behind. Unlike Tomas, Leslie is not letting her physical stature affect her feelings of self-esteem and has expanded her circle to reflect her burgeoning interests and goals. Parents and other adults can keep Leslie engaged by supporting her love of learning and her work with various causes, and also by making sure her social development moves apace so she does not become someone who is "all work and no play."

MARIA

Outgoing and verbally expressive, 17-year-old Maria is at home with all kinds of people. Her social skills are unbeatable, and she has a knack for seeming to hang on every word someone says. People gravitate toward Maria because of her natural warmth and gift of gab. Her parents are proud of her popularity and her social ease, which they believe will open many doors for her in college and future life—so they don't push her so much to get better grades. And, truth be told, she can usually talk her way out of most situations, especially with teachers and authority figures. For all her verbal dexterity, though, Maria can also be scattered organizationally and can rarely see anything to completion. She has problems thinking through all the steps in making a plan and gets distracted easily. She makes decisions impulsively, without thinking about their implications.

MARIA is socially high-functioning, someone who is way ahead in social and interactive skills. She is also endowed with a strong sense of who she is and how she can make her personal strengths work for her. However, her glibness can mask the fact that her complex thinking skills and logic may not be developing at the same pace. Teachers and other adults need to be aware of young people like Maria—those who can talk rings around most people, but whose cognitive functions might be immature. Maria's decision-making and planning skills can be helped along by giving her projects with written or visual content that promote accountability.

TYLER

Tall and with a lifeguard's build, 16-year-old Tyler excels at sports and in the classroom. He likes to exercise his brain and especially enjoys memorizing and dealing with facts. Absolutes make the most sense to him, as Tyler prefers the neatness of black-and-white thinking. What makes Tyler a little uncomfortable is hypothetical situations and "what ifs"—if you can't see it or prove it, in Tyler's mind, then it doesn't exist. This kind of thinking serves him well in sports and doing what the coach says, but he has more trouble when asked to anticipate what the other team members are going to do. Sometimes, with his friends, it is the same way—he thinks things out to a rational conclusion but has difficulty when things stray from what should logically be happening. He also has trouble putting himself in other people's shoes and empathizing with their situations.

TYLER is physically and academically developed, but cognitively he has not moved beyond the level of a concrete thinker, which usually begins around 7 and ends at age 12. Concrete thinkers think logically and are well-organized, but cannot juggle abstract concepts or multilevel thinking. His cognitive development has slowed his social development as well, since he does not think beyond his self-orientation (his values, passions, and needs) to take other people's thoughts and feelings into consideration. Involvement in service learning—which often includes activities that help teens reflect on their service—could help Tyler develop empathy. Adults can also help build Tyler's capacity to recognize and empathize with the perspectives of others by using such "feelings" statements as, "Your friend seems really (worried, upset, discouraged)."

CONCLUSION

CHAPTER 8

Healthy development happens

We invite people of all ages to appreciate the marvel of what it is to be an adolescent. At no other time in life do human beings develop so rapidly, in so many different ways. The teen years are when children grow to full adult size, become capable of reproducing, develop thinking skills that allow them to philosophize about life and plan complex events, and develop the emotional capacity to empathize with and make great sacrifices for others.

The Guide has presented several key ideas supported by research. First and most fundamentally, the rapid changes of adolescence are normal. Most adolescents and their families successfully navigate and enjoy these years. The swiftness of the changes, though, can be confusing and make both teens and adults uncertain of what to do. Knowing what adolescents typically experience emotionally and physically can help resolve worries about whether a teen is on track and whether his or her behavior is reasonable.

The second key idea is that regular, healthy development is uneven.

Physical, emotional, and cognitive development are not always in sync. The Guide has described how it is completely normal for one area of development to be ahead of others. Because development happens unevenly, growth in one domain can place teens in situations they are not ready to handle until they catch up in other areas. Teens need reassurance that they will, indeed, catch up to their peers—or that their peers will catch up to them. Teens also need support and limit-setting from adults to keep them safe.

Third, young people develop positive attributes through learning and experience. Although physical and sexual development happens automatically given adequate nutrition, social and cognitive development does not. These must be nurtured. There is tremendous variation across cultures regarding what is expected socially of young people, but all cultures need to provide the opportunities for young people to experience, learn, and practice competence, connection, character, confidence, and caring.

The final key idea in the Guide is that development happens wher-

ever young people spend time—in their homes, at school, in after-school programs, at work, with friends, and while spending time on the Internet or watching TV. Development does not stop at the doorway of the institutions specifically designed to promote it, namely schools and places of worship. Parents know this well and often worry about fighting a tide of cultural influences over which they have no control.

Yet, as the Guide has described, parents and caring adults often underestimate their capacity to promote young people's development. Because of their developmental stage, young people stop letting adults know that they are important in the young people's worlds, or, for that matter, that the adults even matter. But teens consistently report, and research confirms, that adults remain essential as caregivers, role models, educators, and mentors. It is our hope that through better understanding of adolescent development, adults will feel confident and inspired to continue their indispensable work of fostering the next generation.

RESOURCES & FURTHER READING

If you would like to delve deeper into the topics presented in *The Teen Years Explained: A Guide to Healthy Adolescence,* the following publications provide additional information and resources.

Adolescent Development

You and Your Adolescent
Laurence Steinberg, PhD, and Ann Levine
Harper Collins, 1997, 432 pp.

Your Adolescent: Emotional, Behavioral, and Cognitive Development Through the Teen Years
David B. Pruitt, MD
American Academy of Child and Adolescent Psychiatry and Harper Collins, 1999, 376 pp.

Why Do They Act That Way? A Survival Guide to the Adolescent Brain for You and Your Teen
David Walsh, PhD
Simon & Schuster, 2004, 276 pp.

The Female Brain
Louann Brizendine, MD
Broadway Books, 2006, 280 pp.

Raising Cain: Protecting the Emotional Life of Boys
Dan Kindlon, PhD, and Michael Thompson, PhD
Ballantine Books, 2000, 320 pp.

How to Talk So Teens Will Listen & Listen So Teens Will Talk
Adele Faber and Elaine Mazlish
Harper Collins, 2005, 224 pp.

Physical Development

Planned Parenthood
www.plannedparenthood.org

Sexuality Information and Education Council of the United States
www.siecus.org

Washington State Department of Health Physical Growth and Development Adolescent Health Fact Sheet
http://www.doh.wa.gov/cfh/adfactsheets/whatsup_physicalgrowth.htm

University of Minnesota Extension. "Family: Understanding Youth"
http://www.extension.umn.edu/topics.html?topic=3&subtopic=140

American Psychological Association. Developing Adolescents: A Reference for Professionals (PDF format)
http://www.apa.org/pi/cyf/develop.pdf

Kidshealth.org: Parents' Section
http://kidshealth.org/parent/

Brain Development

National Institute of Mental Health. Teenage Brain: A work in progress (Fact Sheet): A brief overview of research into brain development during adolescence.
http://www.nimh.nih.gov/health/publications/teenage-brain-a-work-in-progress-fact-sheet/index.shtml

American Academy of Child and Adolescent Psychiatry. Facts for Families: The Teen Brain: Behavior, Problem Solving, and Decision Making
http://www.aacap.org/cs/root/facts_for_families/the_teen_brain_behavior_problem_solving_and_decision_making

Harvard Magazine. A Work in Progress: The Teen Brain
http://harvardmagazine.com/2008/09/the-teen-brain.htmll

Body Image

Child Study Center. Teens and Body Image: What's Typical and What's Not
http://www.aboutourkids.org/files/articles/mar_apr_2.pdf

NYU Child Study Center. Encouraging Positive Self-Image and Healthy Self-Esteem
http://www.aboutourkids.org/articles/encouraging_positive_selfimage_healthy_selfesteem

Department of Health and Human Services. Body Image and Eating Disorders
http://www.girlshealth.gov/emotions/bodyimage/index.cfm

The Nemours Foundation. Body Image and Self Esteem
http://kidshealth.org/teen/your_mind/body_image/body_image.html

Obesity: Nutrition and Exercise

The Nemours Foundation. When Being Overweight is a Problem
http://kidshealth.org/teen/food_fitness/dieting/obesity.html

Associated Press. Girls Who Feel Unpopular May Gain Weight
http://www.intelihealth.com/IH/ihtIH/EMIHC000/333/8895/651533.html

UCLA Health System. New Factor in Teen Obesity: Parents
http://www.uclahealth.org/body.cfm?id=403&action=detail&ref=1145

Centers for Disease Control. Healthy Youth: Physical Activity
http://www.cdc.gov/HealthyYouth/physicalactivity/index.htm

Centers for Disease Control. Healthy Youth: Nutrition
http://www.cdc.gov/HealthyYouth/nutrition/index.htm

Cognitive Development

American Academy of Child and Adolescent Psychiatry. Normal Adolescent Development: Part 1
http://www.aacap.org/cs/root/facts_for_families/normal_adolescent_development_part_i

American Academy of Child and Adolescent Psychiatry. Normal Adolescent Development: Part 2
http://www.aacap.org/cs/root/facts_for_families/normal_adolescent_development_part_ii

American Psychological Association. Developing Adolescents
http://www.apa.org/pi/cyf/develop.pdf

Drugs and Alcohol

Centers for Disease Control. Alcohol and Drug Use
http://www.cdc.gov/HealthyYouth/alcoholdrug/index.htm

The Nemours Foundation. Drugs and Alcohol
http://teenshealth.org/teen/drug_alcohol/

American Academy of Child and Adolescent Psychiatry. Teens: Alcohol and Other Drugs
http://www.aacap.org/cs/root/facts_for_families/teens_alcohol_and_other_drugs